THE GYPSY FIDDLE

THE GYPSY FIDDLE

And Other
Tales Told by the Gypsies

JOHN HAMPDEN

Illustrated by Robin Jacques

Introduction by Jan Yoors

THE WORLD PUBLISHING COMPANY
New York and Cleveland

Published by The World Publishing Company
110 East 59th Street, New York, N. Y. 10022
Manufactured at World Publishing Press,
a division of The World Publishing Company, Cleveland, Ohio
Library of Congress catalog card number: 70-82772
Text copyright © 1969 by John Hampden
Illustrations copyright © 1969 by Robin Jacques
Introduction copyright © 1969 by Jan Yoors
Designed by Jack Jaget

1513767

FOR
CLARE ROSALIND
ANOTHER DAY

CONTENTS

CONTENTS

INTRODUCTION

The Gypsies are one of the most mysterious and little known peoples on earth, even though they often live at our very doorsteps. They call themselves the *Rom*; and all those who are not Rom they call *Gaje*, or foreigners, without making much distinction between them. The Gypsies can be found all over the world. The tales told in this collection were first heard and recorded in England, Wales, Poland, Slovakia, Bukovina, Romania, Bulgaria, Transylvania, Hungary, Turkey and Syria.

9

INTRODUCTION

Nobody knows exactly how many Gypsies there are. Available census figures are unreliable, partly because they were taken in each individual country at widely different years and also because Gypsies are nomads; they either may have avoided being counted or, in the typically erratic Gypsy fashion, may have allowed themselves to be counted several times over! Large numbers of them hold citizenship in the countries they live in, for example in the United States, and because of this it proves difficult to single them out as Gypsies. Rough estimates, however, indicate a population of one million in the U.S.S.R.; one quarter of a million in Hungary, Romania, and Bulgaria; about 200,000 between Greece and Turkey; 150,000 in Czechoslovakia and Poland; 120,000 in Yugoslavia; probably close to 200,000 in the United States; and about 40,000 to 50,000 in France and the same in Spain. Prior to and during World War II the Germans persecuted the Gypsies as relentlessly as they did the Jews and exterminated over half a million of them.

In the twentieth century the Gypsies still live much as they did many hundreds of years ago, when they left their homes in northeast India. We don't know why they left, and the Rom themselves have kept no memory of it either.

Even though they are dispersed all over the earth they still speak a common language of their own called *Romanes* or, in English, Romani, which is closely related to some of the languages spoken in northern India today, and is derived from ancient Sanskrit. The Gypsies try hard to keep their language secret, and a knowledge of Romani is the magic key which grants entry to Gypsy communities the world over. As in the folk and fairy tales, the Rom provide generous hospitality and any kind of assistance that may be needed to any Romani-speaking visitor.

The Gypsies are nomads, but they often adapt their way of traveling and living to the countries through which they pass, for the duration of their stay. In England, in France, in Germany, in the Low Countries, and in parts of Hungary they live in what have become accepted in the West as their traditional caravans or covered wagons, which they call *vurdon*. The vurdon is a small wooden house on high wheels, pulled by horses. Inside there is a stove for cooking and heating, beds, a table and chairs.

In other parts of the world—in Turkey or Afghanistan, for example—they live in tents. When they move they pile their tents, feather beds, cooking pots, and cauldrons onto four-wheeled carts. In Greece and in Spain they often use donkeys for transportation. In India they travel in massively built two-wheeled carts pulled by bullocks. In Mexico and in South America they also live in tents, bought from army and navy stores, but they move about in open trucks. And in the United States the Gypsies travel in limousines, preferably Cadillacs.

The Gypsies are a healthy people even though they often look less clean than house-dwellers because of the lack of washing or laundering facilities. They have exceptionally strong white teeth and expressive dark eyes, and they move with feline ease. They are exuberant and gay and their voices are often loud, for they live in the open and have to shout above the wind and over fair distances to be heard. They like to walk barefoot in order to "feel the earth," as they say. They prefer squatting on their haunches to sitting on chairs. Everywhere around the world the Gypsies dress in bright colors. The women wear long skirts of flowered material, their long, shiny blue-black hair in braids. They love to wear abundant gold jewelry. The food they cook is highly spiced and they prefer roast meats to vegetables and fruits. They rarely eat sweetmeats or candy. They are generally known for their total lack of routine or regularity of any kind, and because of this they are thought undependable by the Gaje. They eat when hungry and sleep when tired. They observe no particular day of rest like Sunday, or the Sabbath, but will take advantage of almost any occasion to throw a party and "celebrate." The Rom like to travel and congregate in groups of several families, and since their families tend to be large, this may mean anywhere from fifty to a hundred people. Their dream is to find campsites with plentiful grazing for their horses, with easy access to running water for cooking, bathing, and washing, and nearby a forest where they can gather wood for their fires. In the warm season they sleep on the ground under the open sky, between huge feather beds covered in gaily colored flowered materials.

In view of the mystery and secretiveness of the Gypsies, you may wonder how I know about them. It is because as a boy of twelve years, in Europe, I left behind my loving parents and a younger sister, my comfortable home and the culture in which I had grown up, in order to join the Gypsies.

Gypsy children my own age offered me their friendship and asked me to stay and travel with them, but their parents would not hear of it. They refused to allow me to follow them on their wanderings. They explained that in many countries there were stories—untrue stories, they emphasized—about Gypsies stealing small children, sometimes told by the Gaje parents to their children to frighten them when they were naughty. The Gypsies said, very reasonably, that if they allowed me to stay people would think I was one of those "stolen children." And besides, wasn't I supposed to attend school?

One day, however, a Gypsy chief called Pulika adopted me, and for the next ten years I lived with him and his family, which became my family too. I learned their language and lived as they did. I learned to think as one of them so that I used to say, and sometimes still do, "We, the Rom . . ."

I was very happy with the Rom and loved my Gypsy brothers and sisters. My oldest brother was called Yojo. He was already married and had several small children of his own; then came an older sister, Keja, whom I liked particularly. Then came another brother, Kore, a sister again, Tshaya, about my own age, then two younger sisters, Mala and Boti, who was very dark-skinned and unruly, and last of all the baby brother called Tina.

We, the boys, helped our father, Pulika, by taking care of the horses, riding them bareback to the meadows, watching over them while they grazed, fetching drinking water for them or taking them to the river edge to let them drink. We currycombed them and braided their long manes and tails. Pulika or Yojo would put new horseshoes on them and train them. From them we learned how to talk to the horses, to reassure them, to make them trust us.

At other times we would roam through the woods, or fish and swim in the streams and lakes. We would hunt hedgehogs, *borzo*, and cook them over the open fire, properly seasoned and wrapped in a cover of wet clay. When the clay was baked and had become as hard as pottery, we would smash it open, like a Mexican *piñata*, to eat the hedgehog meat inside that by then was cooked and delicious.

The girls helped their mother with the household chores or by minding the smaller children. They were not allowed to play too far outside the camp or in the woods as we boys were. But, on the other hand, they had the privilege over us to dress in pretty, colorful dresses "like the flowers in the fields."

We moved on almost every day. At times this became tiresome, yet it also held the lure, the hope of meeting other Gypsies along the way or at some crossroads. Meeting other Gypsies in itself was occasion and reason enough for celebration.

During the springtime, summer, and part of the fall, the changing landscape, the campfires, the horses kept us busy, fascinated, and happy. There were, of course, cold and rainy days, when we had to stay inside the caravan, which was really too confined to hold us all comfortably. Outside, the campsite turned to mud. But the winters were worse still. Traveling became exceedingly difficult and often impossible because of snow and frost. Then we had the compensation of sitting together and listening to folk tales. We sat or sprawled on the big feather beds; the potbellied stove would be red-hot while outside the winds howled and rocked the Gypsy wagons on their high wheels.

The folk tales, which in Romani we call *paramitsha*, are always told by one particular storyteller to whom these stories "belong." If someone displays a special gift for story-telling, one of the old ones may as an exception "give away" one of his tales. These tales are told and retold in exactly the same words and even the same sequence, almost as if they were written down and read aloud.

Many of these stories may very well have been borrowed and adapted from various other populations among whom the Gypsies have lived during the many centuries of their migration. It is equally possible that some folk tales told by the Gaje, the non-Gypsies of a specific area, were in fact "passed on" by the Gypsies or that they were borrowed by

14

the Gypsies from one people and "given away" again to
another. In turn the elusive, mysterious Gypsies themselves
have inspired many writers, poets, composers and play-
wrights, scholars and linguists. In all, over six thousand
works of various kinds have been devoted to them, yet their
secret life remains largely untouched and unrevealed.

Besides the *paramitsha*, or true folk tale, the Gypsies have
another extensive but unrecorded "literature"—oral tradi-
tion would be a more correct description—consisting of
didactic tales of experience, which they call *swatura*. These

are supposed to be accounts of things that happened to the person telling the stories, and depict far-off countries through which the Rom traveled in the past. Aside from the pure pleasure of storytelling and of listening to them, these stories are intended to teach the younger generation, or even those older ones who have not been to these particular parts of the world, how the Gaje there live, think, and react to the Gypsies. They tell of the Gaje languages and teach how to cope with specific situations and emergencies. They also tell about other Rom they met along the roads of the world and how they live and love and sing and dance and celebrate life. They tell of the generous Rom and of the mean ones too, of the valiant sons and the virtuous and beautiful daughters. In this fashion the Rom knew about each other long before actually meeting each other, even though they were still separated by oceans and by thousands of miles.

The Gypsies also express themselves in songs. These are called *djilia*. They deal mostly with epic aspects of the life of the Rom, often sharing the same subject matter as that of the tales of experience, but they are more formalized and poetic in expression. Unlike the tales which belong to certain specific owners, the songs can be sung by anyone.

Because I was lucky enough, and willing, to stumble into this marvelous, secret, inaccessible world of the Rom, I want to preserve and to share with you, together with the folk tales of the Gypsies, the vision of their incredible existence in the world today. Theirs is a world of fantasy that nevertheless truly exists, to remind us how life might be, even if for most of us, as yet, it cannot be.

JAN YOORS

New York, 1969

A LITTLE BULL-CALF

A Story from England

The world has turned over since those days, just as you might turn it over with a spade. It's a different world now. In those days animals could sometimes talk and trees could speak too, and there were witches and dragons about.

And in those days there was a lad who lived in a very poor house with his father and mother. One day his father gave him a little bull-calf, and he got very fond of it, so they were a happy family.

But presently his father died and his mother married again. His stepfather was a bad man who hated him and hated the little bull-calf too. One day the stepfather said, "Tomorrow I will kill that calf of yours, and we'll eat it."

Then the lad said to the bull-calf, "We must run away We must go out into the wide world to seek our fortune."

So, as soon as his mother and his stepfather were fast asleep, he got up and crept out of the house. He let the little bull-calf out of its shed, and they set out into the wide world to seek their fortune.

They walked all night and in the morning the lad went to a farmhouse and begged a crust of barley-bread. He broke it in two and gave half of it to his little bull-calf.

Presently they came to another farmhouse, so the lad went to the door and begged a piece of cheese. When he came back with it he wanted to give half of it to the bull-calf.

"No, thank you," said the little bull-calf. "My time has come. I am going across this field to the wild wood, where there are tigers, leopards, wolves, monkeys, and a fiery dragon. They will come to fight with me and I shall kill all that come except the dragon. That will kill me."

"Oh no," cried the lad, bursting into tears. "Oh, my little bull-calf, I hope it won't kill you. I don't want it to kill you."

"Yes, it will," said the little bull-calf. "There is no other way. And the dragon will kill you too if you don't do as I say."

"What am I to do?" said the lad.

"You must climb into that tree. Then no animal can get near you except the monkeys. When the monkeys come you must say to them, 'I will squeeze you as I squeeze this lump of flint stone.' Then you must squeeze the cheese until the milk runs out of it. The monkeys will think you have the strength of a giant and they will go away. Then the dragon will come, and when it has killed me it will go rampaging on, and you must climb down from the tree and take one of my horns. It will kill anything you hit with it. You must find the dragon and kill it with my horn and cut out its tongue and take that away with you."

"Yes, I will, I will," cried the lad, still weeping. He hugged the little bull-calf. Then he climbed high up into the tree.

Soon the monkeys came and began to climb the tree.

"Look," said the lad to the first monkey, "if you come after me I will squeeze your heart as I squeeze this flint stone," and he squeezed the cheese until the milk ran out of it.

"If he can squeeze the juice out of a flint stone," said the monkey to itself, "he must be as strong as a giant. This is no place for us." So down they all went and ran back into the wild wood.

Then a tiger came, growling and spitting, and the little bull-calf fought with it and killed it with its long, strong horns.

Then a spotted leopard leaped out of the wild wood, and the little bull-calf fought it and killed it with its long, strong horns.

Then three wolves came howling out of the wild wood, and the little bull-calf fought with them all and killed them all with its long, strong horns.

And all the time the lad was watching from the tree, clapping his hands and calling out, "Well done, my little bull-calf! Well done!"

But then came the dragon, rampaging through the wild wood, breathing fire and smoke. It flicked its long, fiery tongue like a great spear at the little bull-calf and killed it stone dead. Then it went rampaging back into the wild wood.

The lad climbed down from the tree. He took one of the little bull-calf's horns, and he said, "Good-bye, my brave little bull-calf," and went sadly on his way across the fields.

Presently he came to a tall tree which stood near the wild wood, and there was a beautiful girl. She wore diamonds in her hair, and a long shimmering robe of red silk. But she was chained to the tree with an iron chain around her waist, padlocked at one side.

"Greetings, fair lady," said the lad, doffing his cap politely. "Why are you fastened to the tree? Let me free you."

"You can't," she said sadly. "Only the king, my father,

has the key to this lock. He loves me, but he has chained me here to be eaten by the dragon. It is the only way to stop the dragon from destroying all our kingdom. Our bravest knights have fought with the dragon and it has killed them all. Only a princess will satisfy it and make it go away. There is no escape for me."

That very minute they heard the dragon, roaring and rampaging through the wild wood. They could smell the trees and bushes burned up by its fiery breath.

"There it is," cried the princess. "Go away, young man. Be quick. You cannot save me. Save yourself. The dragon will scorch you to death. Run!"

"No," said the lad, "I will kill the dragon."

He hid behind the nearest tree. The dragon came roaring out of the wild wood, breathing out fire and smoke. It stopped to look at the princess. Then the lad ran at it from the side and with one stroke of the little bull-calf's horn he killed it dead. But as it died it turned and bit off the little finger of his right hand.

The princess burst into tears. The lad went to her and she clung to him. "Oh," she cried, "You have saved me. You have saved the kingdom."

He helped her to dry her tears with her silk handkerchief. Soon she was smiling at him. She tied up his bleeding hand with her handkerchief. She took off one of her diamond rings and slipped it on his finger.

"My father will come at sunset," she said, "expecting to find me dead. Stay with me, so that he can thank you and reward you properly."

The lad shook his head. "No," he said, "it's not for the likes of me in my old rags to talk to a king. I shouldn't know where to put myself."

The princess looked at him and thought what a fine, tall, good-looking lad he was. He looked at her and thought how sweet and beautiful she was. But he was too shy to stay.

He cut out the dragon's tongue and stuffed it into his girdle as the bull-calf had told him to do. He doffed his cap to the princess and went on his way across the fields.

At sunset the king came with his lords and ladies. When they found the princess safe and the dragon dead, how happy they were! The king kissed his daughter, and set her free, and she told him what had happened. Then he led her back to the palace. There they held a great feast, with all manner of good things to eat and drink.

Next day the king sent out heralds to proclaim everywhere that the young man who had the dragon's tongue and had lost the little finger of his right hand should come to the palace and marry the princess.

Great lords and fine gentlemen came hurrying from all parts of the country. They had all chopped off the little fingers of their right hands. They all brought cows' tongues or wolves' tongues or some other animals' tongues. The princess looked at these young men and sent them away. She saw that they were all cheats, and she had set her heart on the lad who had saved her.

This went on, day after day. At last the lad himself came in his rags, with the dragon's tongue in his girdle and the princess's diamond ring on his finger. He felt he could not stay away from her any longer.

All the lords and ladies and fine gentlemen stared at him and whispered to each other. They would have thrown him out if they had dared.

The princess took the king's arm. "That is the brave lad!" she cried. "That is the man I must marry!"

"Well," said the king. "If that's the young man who killed the dragon you must marry him. But let him prove it."

The lad came up to the throne and bowed low to the king and the princess. He showed the dragon's tongue and the princess's diamond ring with her name inside it. He showed where his little finger had been, and the princess's silk handkerchief.

"There's no doubt about it," said the king. "Do you want to marry the princess?"

"With all my heart," answered the lad.

So married they were, and very happy they were, and when at last the king died the lad became king in his place.

THE GOLDEN BOX

A Story from Wales

Once upon a time there was a lad who lived all alone with his father and mother in the middle of a great forest. His name was Jack. He was very lonely, for he had never seen anybody except his father and mother. Not another boy, not a girl, not anybody. But he knew there were other people in the world because his father had a lot of books and he had read them all.

He got so tired of being lonely that he couldn't put up with it any longer. One day when his father was out cutting wood he said, "Mother, I want to go out into the world to see some other people. There's nothing here but great trees all around us. I shall go mad if I stay here."

You can be sure his mother didn't want to lose him. But she was a wise mother, so she said, "Well, Jack, if you feel like that you must go."

She gave him her blessing and a large honey cake to eat on the way. Then he kissed his mother and set out.

He hadn't gone far before he met his father. "Where are you off to, my son?" said his father.

Jack told the old man, and he was very sad, but he said, "Well, Jack, if you really want to go you must go." So they said good-bye and parted.

Then his father called him back. He took a little golden box out of his pocket. "Take this, my son, and keep it very carefully. Open it if you're ever in danger of losing your life. But not till then."

Jack thanked his father, and put the golden box in his pocket, and off he went. Very soon after that he ate his cake, but he went on walking till it was nearly dark. By that time he was tired and hungry, so you can guess how glad he was to see the lights of a house. He found a little door and knocked at it. He felt frightened.

A pretty maidservant opened the door. "What do you want?" she said.

Poor Jack, he'd never seen a girl in his life before. He was very scared. He went red in the face and he could hardly speak. Still, he managed to say that he was looking for somewhere to sleep.

"Come in," said she, for she liked the look of him. She set a chair for him at a table near the fire. "You must be hungry," she said.

"Indeed I am," said he. So she brought him good beef and bread and beer, and you can be sure he tucked in.

Now the master of that house had a very beautiful daughter named Glenys. She heard voices in the kitchen, and what should she do but come in to see who was there. Jack stood up and looked at Glenys, and she looked at him, and there they were, both deep in love.

Jack couldn't say a word, and she couldn't say a word. She ran out of the kitchen. She had no mother, so she ran to her father and said, breathless, "Oh, Father, there's such a beautiful boy in the kitchen!"

The father saw at once how she felt, and he was very angry. But he wasn't going to show it. He said to himself, "I'll get rid of that young man," and off he went to the kitchen.

"Good evening," said he to Jack.

"Good evening, sir," said Jack to him.

"What are you doing here?" said he to Jack. So Jack told his story.

"What can you do?" said the father. That took Jack aback. "Oh, well, sir, oh, anything." All he meant was that he could do any odd jobs about the house.

"Aha," said the father, "you must be a very clever young man. Well then, by tomorrow morning you must make a great lake in front of this house, with some of the biggest warships in the world sailing on it. And at eight o'clock one of the warships must fire a royal salute. If you don't do it, well, that's the end of you." Then he went away.

Jack was so tired he couldn't think of anything to say. The maid showed him where to go. He said his prayers and tumbled into bed and fell fast asleep at once.

When he woke up it was nearly eight o'clock. He remembered what Glenys's father had said and sat up with a jerk. Then he remembered the little golden box his father had given him. "I'm near enough to death now," he thought.

He took the box out of his pocket, and opened it. Three tiny men jumped out on to the bed. They were all dressed in red and had red hats like church steeples. They stood in a row and bowed to Jack. Then they said, "Master, what do you want us to do?"

Jack told them about the lake. They vanished.

Jack lay back on the bed. It was a very comfortable bed.
Soon a clock in the house began to strike eight. At the last
stroke there was a noise like thunder. Jack ran to the window. The valley had turned into a lake, and seven big warships were sailing about on it. The biggest was firing its
cannon. Jack counted. Twenty-one guns! A royal salute!

Suddenly the little men were running across the bed.
They got into their box. Jack said "Thank you" to them
and put the box back into his pocket. Then he went down-
stairs.

There was the father waiting for him. "Well, young
man," said he, not quite so fierce now, "you've done well.
But you want to marry my daughter, don't you?"

Jack blushed and he gulped out, "Oh, sir, yes, sir,
please!"

"Then there are two more things you must do. But first come and have breakfast."

He took Jack into the breakfast room. Jack sat down at the table but he couldn't eat anything because he was looking at Glenys, and she couldn't eat anything because she was looking at him.

Then the father said to Jack, "By tomorrow morning you must cut down all the big trees at the back of the house."

This time Jack wasn't frightened. He had his little men. He told them what to do and it was done.

Then the father said, "You've done well so far, Jack, but now I want a splendid castle, standing on twelve golden pillars. You must build it by tomorrow morning. And it must be guarded by soldiers in red uniforms and brass helmets, and at eight o'clock tomorrow morning they must all present arms."

Once again Jack told his little red men and it was done.

Next he asked them for money. They brought him a sack full of gold coins. He bought some fine clothes for himself and got a servingman to look after him.

Now Glenys's father agreed that she and Jack should get married, so married they were, with great rejoicing. You can be sure they were very happy. At least, they were at first, but then there was trouble.

One day Jack and Glenys and her father went out riding. Jack put on his riding clothes, of course, and for the first time he forgot to put that little golden box into his pocket. He left it in the waistcoat pocket of his other clothes, on the bed.

Well, his servingman came to put the clothes away, and he found the box and he opened it. Out jumped the three little red men. They stood in a row on the bed, and bowed to him, and said, "What do you want us to do, master?"

"This is magic," thought the servingman. "I will see what they can do." So he said to the little red men, "Take the castle, with me in it, far away across the sea to another country."

No sooner said than done. The castle whisked through the air and was gone.

When Jack and Glenys and her father came back from their ride, well, what a to-do! No castle! Glenys's father was very angry, and he thought it must be Jack's doing.

"Now then," said Glenys's father to Jack, "I'm going to take your wife away and you shan't have her back until you bring my castle back. I'll give you a year and a day to find it. If you don't you shall never see her again."

It was no use for Glenys to cry and Jack to complain. Her father dragged her into his old house.

Jack jumped onto his horse and rode off to look for the castle. He rode and he rode, for days and weeks, through fields and woods and sheepwalks, till he came to the kingdom of the mice. He asked the way to the king's palace and rode up to it, as bold as you like, and asked to see the king.

"I'm glad to see you, Jack," said the king, very friendly. "What can I do for you?"

Jack told him about the missing castle, and about his beautiful wife. "Ah," said the king. He took Jack outside and he made a very queer noise. Then all the mice in the world came scampering up, hundreds and thousands and millions of mice. You never heard such a squeaking and squealing, but they all stopped when the king waved his hand.

THE GOLDEN BOX

"Has anyone seen the castle which stands on twelve golden pillars?" said the king.

"No, no, no," squeaked all the mice. The king waved his hand again and they all scurried away, squealing and squeaking louder than ever.

"That's bad," said the king of the mice. "But maybe my brother can help you. He is king of the frogs." So he told Jack which way to go, and said good-bye to him and went back into his palace.

Then the little mouse that was on sentry duty at the palace gate said, "Take me with you, Jack. Perhaps I can help you."

"Jump up, then," said Jack. The little mouse scuttled up one of the horse's legs, which tickled the horse so much that it wriggled and danced and nearly threw Jack. The mouse jumped into Jack's waistcoat pocket and away Jack went.

He rode on, day after day, until at last he came to the palace of the king of the frogs. He asked politely at the gate, and the little frog that was on sentry duty there took him in to see the king.

"Well, then," said the king, when he'd heard Jack's story, "let's go outside."

Outside they went, and the king made a very queer noise. Then all the frogs in the world came hopping and croaking to them, hundreds and thousands of frogs.

The king waved his hand, and they all stopped croaking. "Has anybody seen the castle which stands on twelve golden pillars?" he asked.

"No, Your Majesty," they croaked.

The king waved his hand again, and they all hopped away in next to no time.

31

"I'm sorry we can't help you," said the king to Jack. "But my brother is king of all the birds in the world; maybe he can help you. Birds see a lot, you know. They get about more than frogs do." So he told Jack which way to go, and wished him luck and they said good-bye. Then Jack rode on and on, till he came to the palace of the king of the birds.

Things went much the same there. But when the birds had come the king looked around and said, "Where's Eagle?"

No one had seen Eagle. The king sent up two skylarks to call for him. That brought him in next to no time. He was the biggest bird that Jack had ever set eyes on; a giant of a bird he was.

"Now that we're all here," said the king, "has anyone seen the castle which stands on golden pillars?"

"I have, Your Majesty," said Eagle. "I've just come from that castle now."

"Then all the rest of you can go," said the king, and they all flew away. There were so many of them that they shut out the sun and made the country quite dark for a few minutes. Then they were all gone.

"Now, Jack," said the king, "if you will get onto Eagle's back he will take you to your castle." No sooner said than done. Jack thanked the king and gave him his horse. He climbed onto Eagle's broad back, and away they went, high in the air, over land and sea, until at last they saw the castle, with its twelve golden pillars shining in the sun. Eagle put Jack down nearby.

"Thank you, Eagle," said Jack. The great bird flew away, and Jack stood and looked at the castle and wondered. There must be people inside, and there were guards at the gate. How was he to get his golden box back?

The little mouse put his head out of Jack's waistcoat pocket. "Let me go and get the box," he squeaked. "I'm so small, no one will see me."

Off he went. He crept past the guards when they weren't looking, he scuttled up the steps into the great hall, and he searched from room to room. He was always afraid he might meet the cat, but the cat was fast asleep in front of the kitchen fire, and Mouse didn't go into the kitchen. At last he saw the box on a table in a bedroom. He scrambled up a table leg, and jumped down with the box. Then he sneaked out of the castle so quietly that no one saw him go.

There was Jack, sitting behind a tree, waiting. "Here it is, Jack," squeaked Mouse.

"Oh, thank you, Mouse," cried Jack. He opened the little box and the three little men hopped out.

"What can we do for you, master?" they said.

"Take this castle back to the place it came from," said Jack, "and take me too. But do not take any of the people who are in it now."

The little men made a magic so that all the people in the castle went for a long walk. Jack went in, with Mouse in his pocket, and off they went through the air. A minute later down they came, castle and all, beside Glenys's house.

How happy Jack and Glenys were then! Even Glenys's father was pleased. He'd got his castle back. Then Jack gave Mouse ten pounds of cheese and told the little men to take him back to the king of the mice, and Jack and Glenys and her father lived together happily in the castle by the lake.

THE SUN-KING'S HAIR

A Story from Transylvania

1513767

There was a king in a far country who was very fond of
hunting. One day he went hunting in the forest and
lost all his followers. Then he lost his way. So he was very
glad when he came to a woodcutter's hut and found the
charcoal-burner at home.

The king asked the man the way to the city.

"Noble sir," answered the man, "you could not find the
way by yourself, and I cannot come with you. I have a
baby son who is only three days old and my wife is very
ill. My hut isn't fit for a great lord like you, but if you
stay tonight maybe I can come with you tomorrow."

It was nearly dark, so the king said yes. There was
only black bread and water for his supper and a heap of
dry ferns for him to sleep on, and he couldn't sleep. In the

middle of the night he heard strange voices. He looked through a chink in the wooden wall and could just see the baby in his cradle. Beside the cradle stood three tall fairies, in long white dresses which shone like the moon.

Said one of them, "I wish this boy a misfortune."

Said another, "I will turn his misfortune into good fortune. I will see to it that he marries the only daughter of the king who is now sleeping in the next room."

The third fairy said, "I will see to it that one day he becomes king."

Then all three faded away.

The king was so angry that he gave up trying to sleep. For the rest of the night he sat wondering how he could stop the woodcutter's son from marrying the princess. Then the woodcutter burst into the room, weeping and wringing his hands.

"My wife is dead," he sobbed. "My wife is dead. What am I to do with the baby? How can I bring up a baby all by myself?"

The king saw a chance to get rid of the baby. "That is easy," he said. "I am the king. Let me take the baby and I will have him looked after properly."

·The woodcutter fell on his knees. "Oh, thank you, Your Majesty, thank you," he cried.

"Now, bring the baby, and lead me to the city," said the king, "and I will reward you well."

So they set out for the city, the man carrying the baby in his wooden cradle. When they reached the palace the king gave the man ten gold pieces and sent him away. Then he called for one of his servants.

"Take this child," he said, "and throw him into the river."

The servant didn't like this at all, but he was afraid to refuse. He carried the cradle down to the river and threw it in, baby and all. Then he went sadly to tell the wicked king that it was done.

But the cradle did not sink, for it was strongly made. It floated down the river until a fisherman saw it and took it into his boat. When he found a beautiful baby inside he was overjoyed, for he had no children of his own. He hurried home, and his wife was as pleased as he was. They called the child Nameless and brought him up as lovingly as if he had been their own son.

Twenty years went by. One day the king, riding beside the river, saw Nameless mending nets and was struck by his good looks and his manly bearing. Something made him go into the hut and ask the fisherman, "Is that handsome youth your son?"

"No, my lord," answered the fisherman. "Twenty years ago I fished him out of the river."

It was a terrible shock to the king. He felt sure this young man must be the woodcutter's son. How was he to get rid of him? He sat down on a stool to recover and think it out. Then he said, "I am the king. I want to send an urgent letter to the queen. That lad must take it."

"Oh, yes, Your Majesty," said the fisherman, bowing very low. "Of course he shall, Your Majesty."

The king wrote a letter telling the queen that the young man who brought it must be put to death at once. "If this is not done," he wrote, "a great evil will befall us."

Nameless took the letter and set out for the palace. His road lay through the forest, where he lost his way. He was wandering about, getting very tired and hungry, when he met a strange, tall lady in a long white dress which shone like the moon. He asked her the way.

"I will show you the way," she said. "But come first to my house, to eat and rest."

He went with her gladly. She gave him a good meal, and at once he fell sound asleep. She took the letter out of his pocket and put another one in its place. Then she made a magic. Nameless woke up a few minutes later, and was astonished to find that he was standing at the palace door.

He took the letter to the queen. The princess was there, and Nameless thought her the most wonderful girl in the world, while she thought him the most handsome youth she had ever seen.

The queen read the letter. It said that she must send for the bishop and get him to marry Nameless and the princess at once. She was amazed, but there it was, in the king's handwriting, with his signature at the end. There was nothing else for it. The princess and Nameless were quite willing, and in an hour they were married.

When the king came back he was so angry that he could not speak. He stared and stared at the letter. It was his own handwriting with his own signature at the foot. He guessed that one of the fairies he had seen in the woodcutter's hut had been at work. How was he to get rid of Nameless?

Next morning he said, "Nameless, you must prove that you are worthy to be a king's son. You must go out into the world and bring me three golden hairs from the head of the Sun-King. Then you shall be king after me. But do not dare to come back without them."

Nameless could not help himself. He and the princess said good-bye very sadly, for they now loved each other dearly, and he set out on his quest.

He wandered on till he came to a great black lake and saw a white boat, with an old man at the oars, floating on the water.

"Boat ahoy!" he called. "Will you ferry me across the lake?"

"I will take you across," answered the old man, "if you will promise to bring me word how to escape from this boat. I have been here many years and cannot get away."

"I will if I can find out," said Nameless. So the old man ferried him across the black water.

Soon after that Nameless came to a fine city, and stood in the street wondering which way to turn. "Where do you want to go?" said a man.

"I am trying to find the Sun-King," answered Nameless.

"Then you must come to our king," said the man, and took him to the palace.

When Nameless stood before him the king said, "There was once in this city a magical spring. Anyone who drank its water became young again. But for twenty years it has stopped flowing, and only the Sun-King knows why. I have sent many messengers to him and none has ever come back. If you fare better, please bring us word."

"I will if I can, Your Majesty," answered Nameless, bowing low, and he went on his way.

Some days later he came to another city, and again a man asked him where he was going.

"I am looking for the Sun-King," replied Nameless.

"Then our king would like to see you. Come with me." So they went to the palace.

"Long ago," said the king, "we had a tree which bore golden apples. Whoever ate them became strong and healthy and lived for ever. But for twenty years the tree has not borne a single apple, and only the Sun-King can tell us what to do with it. None of the messengers I have sent to him has ever come back, but you may do better. If you do, will you bring me word?"

"I will," answered Nameless and went on, asking everywhere the way to the Sun-King.

Presently he reached a high mountain, and the path led him to a splendid house. In front of it sat a lady in a long white dress which shone like the moon.

"Where are you going, young sir?" she said.

"I am seeking the Sun-King," he answered.

"Come in," she said. "I am the mother of the Sun-King. Every morning he flies out of this house as a little child. By midday he has grown into a man. When he comes home in the evening he is an old man with a long gray beard."

In the house she asked Nameless to tell her his story, and he told her everything.

"I will ask my son about the man on the lake, and the magic spring and the golden apples," she said. "And I will get you three golden hairs from his head. But I must hide you, for if he finds you here he will burn you up."

She gave Nameless a good meal. Then she hid him in a great cask, where he sat up to his neck in water, so that the heat of the Sun-King should not scorch him to death.

Soon afterward the Sun-King came home, a feeble old man with a shining golden head. When he had eaten he lay down with his head in his mother's lap, and fell fast asleep. She pulled a single golden hair from his head. He woke up and said, "Mother, why won't you let me sleep?"

"Because I had a strange dream," she said. "I saw in my dream a city with a tree which used to bear golden apples. For twenty years now it has borne no fruit at all and the people don't know what to do."

"They should kill the serpent which gnaws at the root

of the tree," said the Sun-King, and very soon he was again fast asleep. Then his mother pulled out another golden hair.

"Mother," he cried crossly, "why don't you let me sleep?"

"Because I had another bad dream," she said, and she told him about the magic spring.

"There is a giant toad blocking the spring," he said. "They should kill the toad." In a few minutes he was sound asleep once more, and she pulled out the third hair.

The Sun-King cried, "Mother, do let me sleep."

"I am sorry, my son," she said, "but my dreams trouble me so much. I have just dreamed of an old man rowing about in a boat on a black lake and he can't escape from the boat."

"Oh," said the Sun-King crossly. "All he's got to do is to get one of his passengers to take the oars and then jump ashore himself. Then he will be free and the passenger will have to stay in the boat."

The lady let him sleep in peace for the rest of the night, and in the morning he flew out of the house, a beautiful child. Then she helped Nameless out of the cask, and dried his clothes and gave him the three hairs. "You heard my son's answers to your three questions," she said. "I have done what I promised to do for you at your birth; you shall be king. And now farewell." She kissed him good-bye.

Nameless thanked her very warmly and set out on the journey back.

When he came to the two great cities he told the kings what the Sun-King had said, and very soon the magic spring was gushing out again and the magic tree's branches were weighed down with golden apples. The first king gave Nameless a heavy gold chain set with the finest diamonds, and the second gave him a large bag of precious jewels, so that now he was as rich as any king's son.

When he came to the black lake the old man refused to take him across. "If you will take me," said Nameless, "I promise to tell you what the Sun-King said, and you will be able to escape from the boat." So he agreed.

When the boat reached the other side of the lake Nameless jumped ashore, and then told the old man to give his oars to his next passenger.

Nameless soon reached home. His beautiful young wife was overjoyed to see him, and the queen was pleased, but the bad-tempered old king was furious when Nameless gave him the three golden hairs. As soon as he heard about the golden apples and the magic spring, however, he was delighted and cried, "I must eat one of those apples! I must drink of that spring!" And off he went at once.

When he reached the black lake the old man handed him the oars and jumped ashore. So the king could not leave the boat, and he must be rowing about there still.

As he never came home Nameless was made king, and he and his queen lived in peace and happiness for many years. And you may be sure that he did not forget to look after the old fisherman and his wife who had brought him up so kindly.

THE YELLOW DRAGON

A Story from Bukovina

There was an old man who lived in a cave with his wife and a crowd of children. They were often hungry and cold, although he went out every day to find work if he could.

One morning he said to his wife, "Please make me a honey cake to take with me. It is getting harder to find work and I may have to go a long way."

So she made him a honey cake and he set off.

He went a long way into the forest and presently he came to a well with a table beside it. By this time he was tired, hungry, and thirsty, so he had a long drink of cold, clear water and ate part of his honey cake. He put the rest on the table and lay down beside it to have a little sleep. When he woke up the table was buzzing with flies, all trying to eat his honey cake. He seized a piece of wood and brought it down on the table with such a bang that it killed a hundred flies.

"Wonderful!" he cried. Dipping his finger in the mud beside the well he wrote on the table, "I killed a hundred with one stroke." Then he lay down again to sleep.

Soon a yellow dragon came along, carrying a water-skin in his great jaws, to get water from the well. He looked as terrible as any other dragon, but he had got so lazy and cowardly that he was afraid to go on rampaging about the country, breathing fire and looking for princesses to eat. He lived quietly in his house with his dragon-wife.

When he read what was written on the table he was

very frightened and said to himself, "If this terrible man wakes up he will kill me."

Just then the old man woke up. When he saw the yellow dragon he sprang to his feet, to run for his life. Then he saw that the dragon was more frightened still, so he looked very fierce and shook his fist at the dragon.

"Oh," cried the dragon, "do not kill me! Let us be friends. Let us swear brotherhood, and I will do you good."

So they agreed to be friends, and the dragon said, "If you will come to my palace my dragon-wife will give us a good meal."

Off they went along the forest path, with the man in front. When the dragon breathed out, the man was blown forward; when he breathed in, the man was dragged back.

"Why do you keep running away from me and then coming back?" asked the dragon.

"Because your breath annoys me," said the man, "and makes me wonder whether to kill you."

"Oh, please don't," cried the yellow dragon. "Please walk behind me."

After this they went on quietly to the dragon's palace, where the dragon whispered to his dragon-wife, "This is a terrible man. He will kill us both if we make him angry. You must give him the best of everything."

The wife set before them roast and boiled and fried meats and chicken and fish, fruit and jellies and sweet cakes, and good red wine. The old man had never had such a feast in his life before, and you may be sure that he ate his fill. "I must stay here," he said to himself.

Afterward the dragon said, "Please, brother, will you take the waterskin to the well and fill it? You are so strong."

47

"Yes," answered the man. He took the bag, and a spade, and off he went to the well. He began digging a trench around it. The dragon heard this, and came hurrying. "What are you doing?" he asked.

"Digging up the well so that I can carry it to your house," answered the man.

"Don't do that," said the dragon. "You will ruin it. Let me fill the skin." And he said to himself, "How strong this terrible man must be!"

So the dragon filled the skin and carried it home, while the man walked beside him.

When they got back the dragon said, "Please, brother, will you fetch a big log for the fire?"

"Certainly," said the man, and off he went to the forest once more.

He did not come back, so presently the dragon went to see what he was doing, and found that he had stripped bark from some of the trees and was making a long rope.

"What is the rope for?" asked the dragon.

"I'm going to tie up the whole forest in a bundle and carry it to your palace on my back, so that you will always have plenty of logs."

"Oh, no," cried the dragon, "please don't spoil my forest. I will carry home a log myself." And to himself he said, "This man must be as strong as a giant." So back they went together, the dragon puffing along with a heavy log in his jaws.

"What are we to do?" whispered the dragon to his dragon-wife. "How can we get rid of him? If I try to drive him out he will kill me. He's as strong as a giant."

"You must wait until he is asleep," whispered the dragon-wife. "Then you must give him such a blow with your big club that it will kill him dead."

The old man overheard them and said nothing, but when they went to their rooms to sleep he did not get into bed. He found a log of wood and put that in the bed. Then he crawled under the bed and went to sleep.

In the middle of the night the yellow dragon got up very quietly, took his club, and crept silently into the old man's room in the darkness. He swung the club over his head and brought it down on the log with all his strength. Then he hurried back to his own room.

"That has finished him," said the dragon to his dragon-wife. "In the morning we will bury him."

The old man crawled out and lit his candle. He put the log under the bed and got into the bed himself. Then he let out a loud yell, "Oh, an insect has bitten me!"

The dragon was so scared that he could hardly speak. At last he said to his dragon-wife, "There! To him a dreadful blow is like an insect's bite. What are we to do with him?"

"Give him a sackful of gold to go away," said the dragon-wife.

So in the morning the dragon said to the old man, "Brother, what will you take to go away?"

"What will you give me?" said the old man.

"I will give you a sackful of gold, brother," answered the dragon.

"Agreed," said the man, "if it's the largest sack you have. And you can carry it to my cave."

The dragon filled his largest sack with gold coins, and followed the man, puffing and blowing under the weight of all that gold. When they came to the cave the dragon threw down the sack, flapped his great wings, and ran away. He was so glad to escape that he even breathed fire once or twice on the way home and scorched a few bushes.

Then the old man took a dozen gold pieces in his pocket and went off to the town, where he bought a strong horse and a large cart. He loaded his family and the gold onto the cart and took them to the town. There they all lived happily in a beautiful house, and they were never hungry again.

ASHYPELT

A Story from Wales

This lad was called Ashypelt. It wasn't his real name, but everybody called him that because he always slept in the ashes behind the stove at home. It was the warmest place in the house.

But he didn't stay at home. One day he said good-bye to everyone and set out to make his fortune. He went along the road and up the hill, and he saw no one. He went on over dales and mountains, where the cock never crowed and the Devil never sounded his horn.

At last he came to a place where there was an old castle and not far away a fine new house. Outside the house there was a man standing, so Ashypelt said to him, "Sir, can you give me a job?"

"Yes," said the man, "I can give you a job. What can you do?"

"Well," said Ashypelt, "I'll try anything you'd like to put me to."

"All right, then," said the man. "I'll give you fifty pounds if you'll sleep in the castle all night."

"That I will," said Ashypelt. Fifty pounds was a fortune to him; he'd never had any money.

Then the man said to Ashypelt, "You shall have a good bag of nuts to crack, and plenty of tobacco to smoke, and a good fire to sit by."

So he took Ashypelt indoors and gave him a good supper. And around about eleven o'clock that night he up and said, "Now, Ashypelt, it's time you came along o' me."

So he took Ashypelt to the castle and he opened the door and he said, "There you are. Go and sit down. Here's your bag of nuts and plenty of 'baccy to smoke. And there's plenty of wood for making up the fire." So he went away.

Now Ashypelt was sitting in front of the fire when, just about the hour of twelve, he heard a lot of noise in the room. He looked behind him at the door, and he saw a man coming in, and the man was naked.

"Come up to the fire and warm yourself," said Ashypelt. "You look very cold."

Now it was a ghost, but Ashypelt didn't know it was. He'd never heard of ghosts. The ghost wouldn't come up to the fire. So Ashypelt went and fetched him.

"Will you have a smoke?" said Ashypelt, and he took and filled a new pipe for the ghost. "Will you crack some nuts?"

The long and short of it was that that ghost smoked all Ashypelt's tobacco and cracked all his nuts, and poor Ashypelt had none.

"You're a very greedy fellow indeed, I must say," said

Ashypelt, "after I've brought you up to warm yourself at the fire."

The ghost said nothing, and just about the hour of two o'clock away he went.

So Ashypelt sat contented by the fire. Next morning the master came in and said, "Are you alive, Ashypelt?"

"Oh, yes," he said, "I'm alive, sir. And a very rude man came here last night. He smoked all my 'baccy and took all my nuts off me."

"Well, come along and have some breakfast," said the master, and took him to the new house.

"Would you like to stay another night, Ashypelt?" he said. "I'd give you another fifty pounds."

"Oh yes, sir," said Ashypelt. He didn't know what ghosts were, so he didn't mind.

All day Ashypelt went up and down in the garden with the man, learning how to dig, and one thing and another, until eleven o'clock came that night.

"Come along, Ashypelt, my lad," said the master. "It's time for you to go back to the castle."

He gave Ashypelt half a pound of tobacco to smoke and a bigger bag of nuts, and off went Ashypelt.

So about the hour of twelve o'clock there was a noise at the door, and he turned around, and there were six of these ghosts coming in. One, which was a skeleton, went and stood in the corner. The others went running up and down the room, pitty-pat, pitty-pat.

"Come up by the fire," said Ashypelt. "You look very cold, running about naked. Come and warm yourselves. There's some 'baccy here, and some pipes. Have a smoke apiece."

So they came and sat down at the fire and helped themselves, all except the skeleton. He went on standing in the corner.

"Here, you," said Ashypelt to him, "you look the coldest of the lot. Why, there's nothing of you except bones."

Ashypelt went and took hold of him, to pull him up to the fire, and he tumbled into pieces, small bits and pieces of bones, all in a heap on the floor.

"Now, Ashypelt," said one of the other ghosts, "if you don't put that fellow together again we'll eat you alive."

So poor Ashypelt went to work fixing one little bit of bone on top of another, and one on top of another, and a hard job it was, but just about two o'clock he got the skeleton together again. Then all the ghosts rose up and left him, and when he came to look for the 'baccy every morsel had gone. He didn't get one pipeful. And there wasn't a nut left, either.

"Well, they're a greedy lot of fellows," he said. But there was nothing he could do about it, so he had a good sleep by the fire.

Next morning the master came again to see if he was alive and take him to breakfast. Afterward he said, "Now, Ashypelt, I'll give you another fifty pounds to stay another night."

Ashypelt didn't like it much, but fifty pounds was such a lot of money to him that he said yes.

So he worked in the garden all day, and at eleven o'clock that night the master said, "Now, Ashypelt, it's time for you to go up to the castle, and tonight I'll give you a pound of tobacco and the biggest bag of nuts you've had yet."

Well, Ashypelt sat himself down by the fire, and had a peaceful smoke, until twelve o'clock. Then he heard such

yelling and screaming and groaning, it made his hair stand
on end. Then the door was flung open and in came a
dead man with his throat cut from ear to ear.

"Come and have a pipe of 'baccy," said Ashypelt,
friendly like.

"No, thank you, Ashypelt," said the dead man. "Come
with me and I'll show you where I lie. My young brother
killed me, so that he could take the castle and the house,
which were rightfully mine. It's my brother who gives you
the money to stay here. He thinks we'll kill you instead
of killing him, but we won't. Now, Ashypelt, you come
with me down these steps."

He took him down steps, and down more steps, and
down more steps, till they came to the dungeons, where
there was a bright light.

"Now, Ashypelt," said the dead man, "I'm the skeleton you knocked all to pieces. You put me together very nicely, and if you'll do one more thing for me I'll make you rich for life. Pull up that flagstone," said he.

"No, sir, thank you, I'd rather not," said Ashypelt.

"Come on," said the dead man. "Lift it up."

So Ashypelt pulled it up, and underneath was a tremendous heap of gold coins.

"Now pull up this flagstone," said the dead man.

Ashypelt pulled it up, and there was the skeleton that he'd put together, lying in a deep hole.

"My brother buried me there," said the dead man. "Now, you do what I want, and all that money is yours, and the house and castle, and I shall never trouble you again as long as you live."

"What must I do?" said Ashypelt.

"Well, tomorrow morning, when you've had your breakfast, you go off to the town and find a magistrate. You tell him the master of the castle has killed his brother and you can show the dead body to prove it. Then, when my brother is brought into court, I'll bear witness."

So Ashypelt went, and the magistrate sent two policemen back with him and he showed them the skeleton in the hole. Then they marched the master off to the town.

When he was brought into court the magistrate cried out for witnesses. Then in came the dead man with his throat cut from ear to ear and told the whole story. The long and short of it was that the master was put in prison for life.

Then Ashypelt went back to the castle, and got a servant or two, and lived there happily. He never saw another ghost. He smoked his 'baccy in peace.

CLEVER PAT

A Story from England

Once upon a time there was a king of England who put an advertisement in all the newspapers, saying that he wanted a new coachman. This man had to know all about horses and be a clever driver. Now this king had a very crooked road leading to his palace. It was full of turns and corners, and very narrow, and there was a ditch on both sides. He'd had it made this way.

All the coachmen knew how hard it was to drive a coach-and-four really fast down that road, so only two of them answered the advertisement, an Englishman and an Irishman.

The Englishman had the first go, and he soon finished up in the ditch.

"That won't do," said the king.

Then the Irishman had a go, and he went, full gallop, all the way down the road.

"Well done, Pat," said the king, "I'll take you on."

"Thank you, Your Honor," said Pat. Then the king took him into the palace, and gave him plenty to eat and drink.

"Now, Pat," said the king afterward, "this evening I'm giving a splendid ball, at nine o'clock, and I shall have to dance with a lot of grand ladies. That always makes me nervous. So I want you to come and stand there, and nod and wink at me when I go by, just to encourage me."

"You can trust me for that, Your Honor," said Pat.

And when the ball started there he was, standing at one side. Every time the king came around, close to Pat, dancing with a grand lady, Pat nodded and smiled and winked at him, and clapped his hands, and whispered, "Well done, Your Honor. You're doing fine." This went on all the evening, and the king was very pleased.

Next morning the king sent for Pat. "You did very well last night, Pat," said the king. "I think I'll marry you to one of my five daughters."

"Thank you, Your Honor," said Pat.

"But first of all," said the king, "there has to be a test. It's always done. If you come through all right you shall marry one of the princesses, but if you don't, well, I must cut off your head."

"Yes, Your Honor," said Pat. "I know that that's the proper way to do things," said he.

"Well," said the king. "The task is this. I've got five white pigeons. They're all out in the yard. You must catch all five, without hurting any of them, and bring them to me in a basket."

"Yes, Your Honor," said Pat.

Off he went to the kitchen to get a big basket with a lid on it. Then he went into the yard, and there, sure enough, were the five white pigeons flying to and fro. Now these pigeons were really the king's daughters. They had magicked themselves into pigeons—clever pigeons at that. Try as he would, he couldn't catch one of them. Not one.

So he stood and scratched his head for a bit. Then he went and got some corn and scattered it just outside the door of the barn, which was open. The pigeons were very hungry, with all that flying to and fro. Down they came and gobbled up the corn.

Then Pat scattered some more, just inside the door. The pigeons came and gobbled that up too. Then he threw down some more, farther inside. The pigeons came in after it, and he slammed the door.

Well, there they were, all five of them inside the barn. It wasn't easy to catch them, but in the end he did, and there they were in the basket.

So Pat went into the palace and he found the king standing in his throne room, with his sword in his hand, all ready to chop off Pat's head.

"Well, Pat," said the king, "have you caught them?"

"That I have, Your Honor," said Pat, very pleased with himself.

"Have you got them all?" said the king.

"Yes, Your Honor," said Pat. "I've got them all five here in this basket."

"Well, open it then," the king told him, "and let me see for myself."

Pat opened the basket, and the pigeons flew out. The king counted them. "There's only four here," said he.

"Faith, Your Honor," said Pat. "I did catch all the five of them."

"That doesn't count," said the king. "You've brought me only four. But I'll give you one more chance, and if you don't bring me the fifth pigeon, sure enough, I'll chop off your head."

"Yes, Your Honor," said Pat, and out he went into the yard again, and there was the fifth pigeon flying around.

Now this pigeon was the king's youngest daughter, and she wanted a word with Pat, private like, so she'd made herself invisible and slipped out of the basket when Pat opened it. Pat didn't know this, of course, so he was very surprised when the pigeon let itself be caught, easy as winking. He put it in the basket and took it to the king.

"Well done, Pat," said he. "We must have a grand feast tonight to celebrate this. I'll go and order it." And off he went, pleased as Punch, leaving Pat and the fifth pigeon alone in the throne room.

Then the pigeon flew onto the throne and called out, "Pat!"

Well, he was properly startled. And when he looked at her she turned into the most beautiful girl he'd ever seen, all dressed in fine silks and shining jewels, with a gold crown on her head.

"Pat," she said, "I'm the king's youngest daughter. I fell in love with you as soon as ever I set eyes on you. Let's get married, shall we?"

"Fine!" said Pat, and he meant it.

So they got married soon after that, and Pat lived happily in the palace with his beautiful wife.

I WAS GOING ALONG THE ROAD

A Story from England

Well, sir, the other day I was going along the road, just quietly, all by myself, and presently I met a man who was deaf and dumb.

"How far is it to the next village?" I asked him.

"Maybe three or four miles," said he, "and steep at that."

So I thanked him, and went on, and very soon I met with a man who was blind.

"What might the time be?" I asked him.

He looked at his watch. "I make it twenty minutes to three," said he.

So I said thank you and went on, and I got out my empty pipe, thinking to light up, but I found I hadn't got any 'baccy. So I went on, sucking at my empty pipe. It wasn't long before I met a man who was naked.

"Can you spare me a fill of 'baccy?" I asked him.

"That I can," said he. "Fill up, and welcome." He took his pouch out of his pocket and gave it to me.

So I filled up my pipe, and he put his pouch back in his pocket, and I thanked him and went on.

After a bit I came to the village, and the first thing I saw was a man with no arms wheeling a sack of potatoes down the street in a wheelbarrow. And the next thing I saw was a man with no legs, running after him as hard as he could and shouting, "Stop thief! Stop thief! Them's my taters you're a-taking!"

Well, there was a fine to-do, but when it was all settled, on I went up the village street. There I found an old, old man, over a hundred years old he was, sitting on a doorstep and crying his eyes out. The tears were running down his face and dripping out of his beard.

"What's up, gaffer?" I asked him.

"It's my grandfather," he said. "My cruel grandfather. He's just got married again and he's turned me out of the house. Boo-hoo!"

Well, I tried to comfort him, and then I went on up the village street, for ten or twelve miles maybe, until I met with a dead man being carried on a stretcher.

As soon as the dead man saw me he opened his eyes. "There's a man that needs a mug of beer," said he.

"Truer words were never spoken. Yes, sir, I don't mind if I do. Thank you, sir."

YOUNG HAPPY

A Story from Bukovina

Young Happy was the happiest Gypsy that never was. He had a grindstone for sharpening things that didn't need sharpening. He used to put it on his barrow and put his wife and children on top of it, and off he would go along the road, faster than all the coaches in the country.

Then Happy got tired of the grindstone. He cut it up to make tent-pegs, and chopped up the barrow to make sausages.

Then his donkey got away. After a week or two he thought he would look for it. So he walked around and about, shouting and calling. Presently he came to a tall tree.

"Here I am, Happy," shouted the donkey. "I'm up the tree. I've been here a week, gathering firewood for you."

Then the donkey came climbing down the tree with the firewood.

Next day Happy went walking with his dog. It started two hares and chased them both. As it ran across a field it ran over a scythe which cut it clean into two pieces. One half of the dog ran after one hare, the other half ran after the other hare. They both caught their hares. Then the two halves of the dog joined up again.

"I've caught them, Happy!" shouted the dog. "I've caught both the hares!" Then the dog lay down and died.

There was a hole in the knee of Happy's breeches. So what did he do? He patched it with a piece of the dog's skin.

Next year the patch split, and the breeches barked at Happy.

Then what did Happy do? He went on being the happiest Gypsy that never was.

MAGIC APPLES

A Story from Wales

There was once an old king of England who was ill for a long, long time, and no medicine did him any good. At last his doctors said, "Your Majesty, only one thing will make you well. You must have some golden apples."

"Where can I get them?" said the king.

"No one knows," said the doctors. "But a royal prince might find them."

So the king sent for his three sons and told them they must go out into the world and bring him some golden apples.

"Yes, Father," they said. They mounted their favorite horses and rode out of London, clip-clop, clip-clop. Soon they came to a place where three roads met.

"I will take the road to the north," said the oldest.

"I will take the road to the south," said the next.

"I will go west to Wales," said the youngest. "I know the Welsh Gypsies, and I speak the Gypsy language, Romani. They will help me."

"Our father sent us out together," said the oldest.

"Let us all meet here in a month and a day," said the second, "and wait for each other."

So it was agreed. They said good-bye and rode off.

The two older brothers didn't do much good for themselves, but the youngest brother, whose name was Valentine, had better luck.

He rode west and he rode west till he came into Wales. There the road passed a large house which stood all alone in the fields. An old man was sitting outside in the sun. He had long white hair and a long red nose, and he looked very fierce. But he spoke kindly.

"Greetings, king's son," he said in Romani.

"Greetings," said Valentine, in Romani. He reined in his horse. "How do you know I'm a king's son?"

"You're the youngest son of the king of England," said the old man, "and you are looking for the golden apples. Come in. I can help you."

Valentine was rather afraid of that fierce-looking old man, but he got off his horse and took it to the stables, and went into the house.

He had a very good meal, with plenty to eat and drink. He had a good bed too, and next morning after breakfast the old man said, "Now, I cannot tell you how to find the golden apples, but my elder brother can, so you must go to him. I will let him know you are coming. Leave your own horse here and take mine. Throw this piece of string between its ears and it will take you to my brother."

The horse went off like a shot out of a gun and galloped day and night until it stopped at a house which stood alone in the fields, and there was an old man sitting outside. He had long gray hair down to his waist, and his teeth curved out of his mouth like tusks. His fingernails and toenails had not been cut for a thousand years. "Welcome, king's son," he said. "My young brother sent me word that you were coming." He spoke Romani like the Welsh Gypsies. "Take the horse to the stables and we will go into the house."

Valentine had a very good meal and a very comfortable bed. Next morning he woke as fresh as a newly caught trout, and after breakfast the old man said to him, "You must travel fast. You must be back here before dark or you will be lost. Take my best horse, and throw this piece of string between its ears. It will carry you to the Castle of Marvels, and there you will find the golden apples. The castle stands in a lake of black water. It is guarded by terrible things. But every day at one o'clock an enchantment is laid on it. Then every living creature in it falls asleep. That is your only chance, for at two o'clock everything wakes up. If you are still there then, you will be torn to pieces or turned into a dreadful monster. I will tell you what you have to do. Listen well." So he told him.

The old man's horse went like the wind. Far and far it went. At last they came to the black water, and there was the Castle of Marvels.

Valentine tethered the horse to a tree and looked at his gold watch. It was a quarter past one. There were three white swans swimming on the black water, and he called to them as the old man had told him to do: "Swans, swans, in the name of the Griffin of the Greenwood, carry me to the castle."

They spread their wings and carried him across the black water. He went in at the great door. It was guarded by four terrible giants, with drawn swords in their hands, but they were all sitting against the wall, fast asleep and snoring.

He came to the next door. Lions and tigers lay across the threshold, fast asleep. He stepped over them and came to the third door, where great poisonous serpents lay in coils. He tiptoed past them into the hall.

There was the grand staircase. He went up quietly and opened a door on the right, as the old man had said. He found himself in a splendid bedroom. On a golden bed lay a princess in a flowing gown of green and silver, fast asleep. She was so beautiful that he stood spellbound,

unable to move. The minutes ticked away and ticked away. . . .

Suddenly he remembered. He looked at his watch. It said ten minutes to two. The princess's watch and handkerchief were on a table beside the bed. He put them in his pocket and left his own in place of them. He bent over the princess and kissed her gently. She stirred but did not wake up.

He went out through the far door and ran down a staircase which led into the kitchen. The fat cook lay flat on her back in the middle of the floor, fast asleep, with a knife in one hand and a fork in the other. He ran out into the orchard. There was the magic tree, heavy with golden apples which shone in the sun. Quickly he filled his wallet.

He ran back through the kitchen. The cook opened one eye and winked at him, but she did not wake up. He sped back by the way he had come, not daring to look at the princess. He ran silently down into the great hall, and out of the castle. The giants were stirring as he passed them.

"Swans, swans, come quickly," he cried. "In the name of the old Griffin of the Greenwood, carry me across."

They carried him across. As he stepped ashore he heard the castle clock strike two. He untethered his horse and leaped into the saddle. Away they went like the wind.

Things were coming after him, Things which hissed and howled and roared. The old man had told him he would be lost if he looked back. He did not look back. For a thousand miles the Things hunted him, hissing, howling, and roaring. But the horse was too swift for them. At sunset he came to the old man's door.

73

"Well done, Prince Valentine!" cried the old man. "Many kings' sons have gone on that quest. You are the first who has come back. Come in!"

"I owe it all to you," said Valentine.

That evening they feasted together, while Valentine told the story of his adventures.

In the morning, after a jolly handshaking, Valentine mounted the younger brother's horse and rode to his house. There he told his story again, and thanked his host. Next morning he rode away on his own horse, and he rode east and he rode east until he came to the place where he was to meet his brothers.

There was no sign of them, and the day was hot and he was tired. So he lay down in the shade of a tree and he hitched his horse to his leg. He put the wallet full of golden apples under his head and went fast asleep.

Very soon the oldest brother rode up, and then the second brother came. Their wallets were full, but the apples were not golden, they were ordinary green apples.

"We have failed," said the oldest brother. "Let us see what Valentine has got."

Very gently he lifted Valentine's head without waking him, and took away Valentine's wallet, and put his own wallet full of green apples in its place.

They looked into Valentine's wallet, and looked at each other, very upset.

"He's got them!" whispered the second brother. "What will our father say to us? He will be furious. He may turn us out of the palace."

"We must take them to him ourselves," said the oldest brother, and off they went.

The sun was setting when Valentine woke up. There was

74

no sign of his brothers. "I cannot wait here all night," he said to himself. He mounted his horse and rode toward London.

Long before he reached it he heard all the church bells ringing merrily, and when he rode into the city people were lighting bonfires and dancing in the streets.

"What's all this about?" he asked a man.

"The king is cured!" cried the man. "He is well again!"

How puzzled Valentine was! He rode to the palace, and there he found the king, looking very jolly, feasting with the queen and the two princes.

"Welcome back, Valentine," cried the king. "Have you brought me golden apples too, like your brothers?"

"Indeed I have," answered Valentine, handing over his wallet.

"Thank you," said the king. Smiling, he looked inside. Then he sprang to his feet in a fury. "Cheat! Impostor!" he roared. "These are *green* apples. How dare you? Do you want to poison me? Guards, take him away! Tell the palace butcher to cut off his head!"

So the guards took Valentine away, but the butcher wouldn't cut off his head. No, not he. He knew the king would be sorry, sooner or later. He took Valentine in a carriage to Epping Forest and left him there.

The poor prince wandered miserably into the forest. Then he saw a big brown bear limping along on three legs. So the prince climbed up a tree to hide.

But the bear limped up to the tree and called out in Romani, "Don't be afraid, sir! I'm a Gypsy in disguise. My name is Jubal. I know you. I've seen you hunting in this forest. You are Prince Valentine. Come down, sir. Then we can be friends."

75

So Valentine climbed down, and told his story. Then Jubal took him to a tribe of Gypsies who were living in tents in the forest. There Jubal took off his furry skin and showed himself as a handsome young Gypsy.

Valentine lived with the Gypsies for months. They were very kind to him. They taught him their dances and taught him to play the Welsh harp. At night they all gathered round the campfire to tell wonderful strange stories until the last of the logs had burned out and it was time for bed. But Valentine was sad at heart.

Then one day something happened at the palace. A splendid golden coach drove up to the gate. In the coach was the beautiful princess of the Castle of Marvels. She wore a sumptuous dress of cloth of gold, and her guards looked very smart in their green uniforms richly embroidered with silver. They all rode black horses.

The king received her gladly and asked what he could do for her.

"Your Majesty," she answered, "I have a gold watch which one of your sons left behind him when he came to my castle to get the golden apples. I want to give it back to him. May I see him?"

"*Two* of my sons brought back the golden apples," said the king, "and here they are."

The oldest came forward, looking scared.

"Have you ever been to the Castle of Marvels?" said the princess.

"Yes," said he.

The princess threw Valentine's handkerchief on the floor. "Then will you walk over that?" said she to the prince.

Well, he tried, but no sooner had he put his foot on it than he fell flat on his face.

76

Then it was the second brother's turn, and just the same thing happened to him.

"Haven't you got another son?" said the princess to the king.

The king hung his head and looked very, very miserable. Then he remembered that the butcher didn't always do what he was told to do. He sent for the butcher. "Did you chop off the prince's head?"

"No, O King," said the butcher. "He's still alive and he's in Epping Forest."

"Then send for him at once," said the king.

They didn't waste any time going to look for the poor Welsh-harping prince. It wasn't long before he was back at the palace. He had a good wash and went in to see the princess.

"Have you ever been to the Castle of Marvels?" said she.

"Yes," said Valentine, smiling at her and she smiling back at him.

"Then walk over this handkerchief," said she.

He walked over it, two or three times. Then he danced on it. Nothing happened to him.

She pulled his gold watch out of her pocket. He pulled her gold watch out of his pocket, and they exchanged them.

Then the princess said to the king, "This is the prince who came to my Castle of Marvels and took away the golden apples."

The two older brothers were so ashamed they hurried out of the room and hid themselves.

The princess smiled at Valentine, and he smiled at her. "You broke the spell on the Castle of Marvels," said she to him. "Will you marry me and come and live there?"

"Very gladly," said he, and next day they were married.

Then they said good-bye to the king and queen, and got into the golden coach and drove off, with all the guards riding behind.

On the way they visited the Gypsies in Epping Forest, to thank them for being so kind to the prince. The princess gave them all rich presents, and asked them to come and stay with her. And they gave Valentine the Welsh harp, so that he could play it in the evenings.

THE LITTLE SNAKE

A Story from Romania

On the edge of a forest lived an old woodman and his
wife. They had never had any children, and the woman
was always moaning and complaining about this. "Who's
going to look after us when we're too old to work?" she
said. Day in and day out she said it.

At last her husband said, "Well, what can I do about
it?"

"Go out into the forest and find us a son," she answered.

He grumbled and grumbled, but next day he took his ax
and went into the forest. He walked on all day, and when
night came he slept in a tree, for fear of the bears and
wolves. His wife had given him a honey cake, and when
he'd eaten this he had nothing left. Next day he went on
again. He did not see a man or woman or a house any-

where. Then he got so tired and hungry that he turned back to go home.

A tree had fallen across the path, and there was a little snake caught under the tree.

"Father, Father, please set me free," cried the snake.

"That I will," said the old man. He levered up the tree with his ax and the little snake wriggled out. The man put it into his pocket and went home.

"Look," he said to his wife, "I've found a son for us."

"What nonsense!" she said crossly. "Who ever heard the like of that? A snake for a son, indeed!"

"Well, he's all we've got," said the man, "and if we're good to him I'm sure he will be good to us."

With a piece of old blanket he made a warm nest for the snake behind the stove, and gave him warm milk. He grew so fast that very soon he could go out to hunt for his food, but he always came home at night, for the old people were both very kind to him.

At last, when he was six feet long, he lifted his head high in the air and said, "Father, it is time for me to get married. I am a prince, so my wife must be a princess. Tomorrow you must go to the king of this country and ask for his daughter in marriage."

The old man beat his breast. "Oh, no," he cried. "If I go to the king and say that, he will cut off my head."

"No," replied the snake, "he won't cut off your head, and you must do as I say. I will give the king anything he wants."

So next morning the old man set off for the king's court.

"All hail, O King," he said, bowing before the throne.

"Thank you, old man. What do you want?"

"I want your daughter's hand in marriage for my son, Your Majesty."

THE LITTLE SNAKE

"What! How do you dare? You are a poor peasant and I
am a king."

"That does not matter, Your Majesty. If you will give
your daughter to my son I will give you anything in the
world you want."

The king laughed and laughed. "This is easily settled,"
he said. "You know the great forest. Cut down all the
trees, plow up the earth, and sow it with maize. When the
maize has ripened, make a cake from some of it and
bring the cake to me. If you do all this by tomorrow
morning I will give you my daughter." He laughed again.

The old man was so frightened that he could not speak.
He bowed low and went home, beating his breast and
weeping.

"Why are you weeping, Father?" said the snake.

The man told him the story, and the snake said, "You
need not weep, my father. I will see to it."

Then the snake went to the edge of the forest; he coiled
himself up, and he thought and he thought. Next morning
he came back with a bag of maize in his jaws. "It is all
done, my father, and now you can make a cake with
this."

The old woman ground the maize and mixed it with
milk. She baked the cake on the stove. The old man
took it to the palace.

The king was so angry that he did not keep his promise.
"There is one thing more for you to do. Make me a
golden bridge from my palace to your house, and make
apple trees and pear trees bearing golden fruit to grow on
the bridge. This must be done by tomorrow morning. If
you do it I will give you my daughter. If you don't I will
cut off your head."

The old man bowed low and went away. "This is too

81

much even for the snake," he thought. He went home
weeping and wringing his hands.

"Why are you weeping, Father?" said the snake.

"I am weeping because of the misery which has come
upon me." He told the snake the story.

"Fear not, Father. It shall be done."

He went out and coiled himself up, and he thought
and he thought, until everything was done.

In the morning the man walked over the golden bridge
to the king's palace, picking golden apples and pears as
he went. He laid them at the king's feet.

What could the king do now? He had to keep his word.
"Go now," said the king, "and fetch your son. Then we
will hold the wedding."

Home went the old man and told the snake.

"Now you must get out your cart and your horses and
take me to the palace," said the snake.

So they drove in the cart over the golden bridge.

The old man walked into the palace with the snake beside him. The king and queen and princess and all the courtiers were waiting, and they were all terrified when they saw that huge snake.

"This is my son," said the old man.

"No, no," cried the king. "She can't marry a snake! I won't have it."

"You must keep your promise," said the courtiers, "or this terrible snake will kill us all."

The princess was trembling with fear. "Will you marry me?" said the snake.

"Yes," she said. She was afraid to say no.

"You have broken the spell," said the snake. He sprang into the air. He turned a somersault. And there he stood, as handsome a young prince as ever was.

The princess was so glad, she threw her arms around him and kissed him.

So they got married that very day, and a happier wedding was never seen.

A WANDERER WITH A DOG

A Story from Slovakia

Long, long ago a wanderer came to a beautiful city and with him came a dog.

The city was in mourning. Black flags flew from all the houses, and black cloths hung in every street. The people were all dressed in black, their faces were pale, and they went about without saying a word.

The wanderer stopped a man and said to him, "Sir, why is your city so sad?"

"Because of the dragon," said the man.

"Which dragon?" asked the wanderer.

"The greatest, most terrible dragon ever seen," answered the man. "It has three heads. It is so huge that it could crush us and our city easily with its terrible claws. Every day it has devoured one of our maidens. Now there is only one left, the king's daughter. After we have given her to the dragon today it will destroy us all."

"Can no one kill the dragon?" asked the wanderer.

"No one," said the man. "All our knights and all our soldiers have gone against it, in vain. It breathed fire from its nostrils and scorched them to death."

"Where is this dragon?" asked the wanderer.

"It lives with its blind dragon-mother in a cave in that mountain." The man pointed to the mountainside.

"My dog and I must deal with this," said the wanderer.

The man looked at the dog and he shook with fear.

"It is a very strange dog," he said.

"Yes, it is a very strange dog," said the wanderer. "It is a dog from the other world. A far stranger dog than you can imagine. We will go to the cave."

They left the city. They climbed the mountain to the cave.

"O evil dragon," cried the wanderer, "come out!"

With a roar which shook the earth the dragon came. Flame and smoke poured from its nostrils.

The dog growled like thunder. The flames could not scorch it. And it grew. It grew larger and larger. It towered above the giant dragon.

"Strike!" cried the wanderer.

With one sweep of a great paw the dog struck the dragon to the earth. It lay there, howling with fear. It breathed fire and smoke no longer.

"You have done evil," said the wanderer. "Now you must swear never to kill maidens or men again, and to leave that city in peace."

"I swear it," whimpered the dragon.

"If you forget your oath," said the wanderer, "I shall come back with this dog and we will kill you."

"I will remember," whimpered the dragon.

Its blind dragon-mother crawled out of the cave. "We will remember," she whined.

The great dog shrank to its former size. The wanderer went back to the city, with the dog running beside him, and he told the people that they were safe. The king threw a rich rope of jewels around his neck. The princess wept and thanked him again and again. All the people cheered him, and that evening there were bonfires in the streets and great feasting and merrymaking.

But the wanderer and his dog had gone on their unknown way.

BATIM THE HORSE

A Story from Bulgaria

There was a king in a far country who kept many fine horses in his stables, for he loved horses and went out riding every day. But the finest horse of all he never rode, and no one was ever allowed to see it except the king himself and the stableboy who looked after it. This was not really a horse at all, but the son of an ogress who was under a spell, and the king knew and looked after it very carefully.

The king had four daughters. One day they came out onto the balcony of the palace, to sit in the sun and do their embroidery. Just at that time the stableboy went into the stable to feed the horse, and while the door was open the oldest princess saw the horse and he saw her, and he fell in love with her at first sight.

The boy gave the horse nuts and sherbet, but he would not eat or drink. The boy ran into the palace.

"O King," he cried, "the horse will not eat, he will not drink."

"Has anyone seen him?" asked the king.

"O King, when I went into the stable all the princesses were on the balcony. Maybe one of them saw the horse."

"We will soon see," said the king.

He called all his daughters to him. He filled their aprons with nuts and he took them all into the stable.

"Now feed the horse," said the king.

The youngest princess offered the horse her nuts, and he would not eat. The next offered her nuts and he would not eat. The third offered her nuts and he would not eat. The oldest princess offered her nuts and the horse ate them all. She brought sherbet and he drank it all.

"He has fallen in love with you," said the king. "Now you must marry him or he will vanish away."

So the horse and the princess were married, and as soon as they were left alone together he turned into a handsome prince, and he told her that his name was Batim. "But I must go on appearing as a horse to everyone but you," he said. "Tomorrow I shall change back into a horse."

Next day Batim said to her, "Tomorrow I shall go out in my human shape, dressed in green clothes, with a green horse under me. I shall ride around the palace. When they see me your sisters will mock you and say to you, "That is the kind of husband you ought to have had. Why did our father have to give you to a horse?" Then you must take care not to tell them that I am your husband. If you do I shall disappear. Then you will have to make shoes of iron and a staff of iron, and search for me everywhere until you find me in the land where my mother lives."

Next day Batim rode around the palace all in green. The sisters mocked his wife, but she did not say a word.

The following day he rode around the palace dressed all in white, with a white horse under him. The eldest princess's sisters mocked her as before, and this time she could not hold her tongue. She said, "But that *is* my husband!" And they all three laughed and would not believe her.

That evening Batim said to her, "Alas, you have betrayed me. Now you must make yourself shoes of iron and a staff of iron and search for me through the wide world until you find me." And at that he disappeared.

Next morning the princess made herself shoes of iron and a staff of iron and set out. She trod the roads wearily for seven months, and at the end of the seventh month she came to a fountain. She sat down beside it to rest. Presently a servant came with a pail and filled it with water.

"What are you going to do with that water?" she asked.

"I am taking it to the castle, to Prince Batim," he answered.

"Will you let me drink some of the water?" she said.

"Yes, lady," he answered. But she only pretended to drink. She dropped her wedding ring into the pail, and the servant did not notice. But when the water was taken to Batim he saw the ring and recognized it.

"Who was at the fountain?" he asked.

"There was a young bride," answered the servant.

"Bring her to me," said Batim.

How glad they were to meet! "But we are in danger," said Batim. "My mother is an ogress and she will want to eat you."

Very soon the ogress came. "Ha," she growled when she saw the princess, "you would make good eating. If you don't want me to eat you, tomorrow you must do this. Tomorrow you must weep and weep until you have filled that tank with your tears." She locked up the princess in one of the bedrooms for the night, and let her out in the morning.

The princess wept and wept, but the tank was hardly moist. Then came Batim. "You silly," said he, "we must take the pail and bring water from the fountain until the tank is full. Then we will get a packet of salt and dissolve it in the water until it is as salt as tears."

So with his help the princess did as he said. Then came the ogress. "Ha," she growled, "my son must have helped you. This is not enough. Tomorrow you must fill forty-one rooms in this castle with feathers, and have as many left over. If you don't I shall eat you." She locked her up again for the night.

Next morning the princess went out to look for feathers. Here she found one, there she found one, and she was crying all the time. Then came Batim. "What is it today?" said he. "Why are you crying?"

"Oh, Batim," she said, "your mother will eat me if I don't fill forty-one rooms with feathers and have as many left over, and feathers are so hard to find."

"Call out, 'Come, birds, come, birds, come! Batim needs you,' " he said. She called, and all the birds of the air came flocking and shed their feathers, until she had more than she needed.

Then came the ogress. "Have you done it, good-for-nothing?" she growled.

"I have done it, Mother," answered the princess.

"My son has helped you," growled the ogress, and locked her up again.

In the morning early Batim took his mother's keys while she was still asleep, and set the princess free. Then the two fled as fast as they could.

Presently the princess looked back. "Your mother is coming after us," she cried. "She is breathing fire and smoke from her nostrils."

Batim turned his wife into an oven and turned himself into a baker. He set to work to light the oven.

Soon the ogress came. "Baker," she growled, "have you seen a man and woman pass this way?"

"No," he answered, "no one has passed."

So the ogress went back. Batim turned his wife and himself into their own shapes, and they hurried on. But the ogress saw them from her tower in the castle and came after them again.

The princess looked back. "Oh," she cried, "your mother is coming again."

Batim turned his wife into a pond, and himself into a duck swimming on the pond.

"Ah," growled the ogress. "If I were sure that that duck is the good-for-nothing princess I could throw a stone and kill her. But the duck may be Batim, and then if I killed it I should kill my son."

So she went back to her castle, and Batim and his wife turned into their human shapes and went on. Again the ogress saw them and gave chase, but Batim saw her coming. He turned his wife into a wild rose bush and himself into a rose on the bush.

Then came the ogress, but she was not angry now. "Batim," she said, "I see that you love the princess truly and cannot live without her. I will harry you no more. I give you both my blessing. May you both drink your soup with a silver spoon and eat your bread from a golden plate."

Then Batim and the princess turned back into their own shapes and the three rejoiced together. When they got to the castle Batim made a wedding feast which lasted for seven days and seven nights, and they all had the most delicious food anyone could imagine.

THE BASKET-MAKER'S DONKEY

A Story from England

Not so long ago Gypsies used to travel with donkeys to carry their things, and there was one old Gypsy who had had the same donkey for years and years and years. It was a great pet of his and he was very fond of it.

This old man earned his living by making baskets. His wife loaded the baskets onto the donkey's back and went around with it, selling the baskets, from door to door.

Well, one day the old man was sitting on the steps of his caravan, weaving his baskets as usual, and the donkey was there beside him. But this day, instead of keeping him company quietly, as it usually did, it kept pestering him, licking his face, pretending to bite his arm, and so on. He kept driving it away, but this was no good. As soon as he sat down to his basket again, back came the donkey, making itself a regular nuisance. He got crosser and crosser, until he couldn't stand it any longer. He picked up a long switch and chased that donkey.

When he caught up with it he let fly with the switch for all he was worth. He gave the donkey such a welt that he cut it clean in two, from head to tail, and the two halves tumbled to the ground. When he saw what he'd done he was in a terrible state. He was very fond of the donkey, and, besides, how was he to sell his baskets if he hadn't a donkey to carry them around to people's houses?

"What can I do? What can I do?" he cried, with the tears rolling down his face.

Then he thought of the withes, the long, supple, willow twigs which he used to tie things up with. He had a great

heap of them. He ran and fetched an armful. Then he stood the two halves of the donkey up, and fitted one half to the other very carefully, and tied them together with willow withes. Then he went and found some clay and daubed it all along the joining, to make the two halves stick together.

"There now," said he, "I reckon I've made a good job of that!"

And so he had. The two halves of the donkey grew together again, it was as good as ever, and it went on working for years after that. What was more, the willow withes took root in the donkey and grew, so when the old man wanted withes he didn't have to go and look for them; he just cut them off the donkey.

I WAS TRAVELING THOSE PARTS

A Story from England

You know, there's old lead-mining shafts in parts of Derbyshire, a-many of them, and hidden away in the bracken, as like as not. Deep shafts that you can fall right into before you know where you are.

Well, I was traveling those parts once, and one morning I took my dog out to see what we could get for dinner. Very soon he started a hare. Away went the hare, and away went the dog after him, and away went I after them. Well, what with watching the hare and the dog I didn't give much heed to where I was going, and all of a sudden, woof, I found myself a-tumbling down one of these old shafts.

It was a narrow shaft, and I banged against the sides all the way down, and it was a long way down, so wasn't

I glad when I hit the bottom. Every bone in my body was broken. I lay there a bit. Then I said to myself, I said, "Well, now I'm underground I might as well see what sort of place it is." So I set out walking.

It's a queer world, down there underground. Everything is different. The first thing I came to was a nice little lake of water, and there was a man with a team of horses plowing on it so that he could plant corn. Next I came to a gentleman's park, and there was a ship sailing on it. After that I got onto a road, and very soon I met a donkey, riding on a man's back. It was beating him something cruel, so I said if it didn't stop I'd knock its head off. That stopped it.

Next I came to an old roadman, sitting by the side of the road with a big heap of stones and breaking them up small to mend the road. He was breaking them with a feather. It was hard work.

After I'd left him I came to a little old cottage, and there I met an old woman carrying water in a sieve. By this time I was getting hungry, so I said to her, "Could you spare me a bit of pudding, ma'am?"

"That I could," said she, "and welcome."

She took me into her garden, and there was a tree with the finest crop of puddings you ever set eyes on.

"Help yourself," said she. "Eat as many as you like."

That was a good square meal, that was, and afterward I had a long drink of water from the sieve, and thanked the old woman, and came away.

I hadn't gone far along the road before I met with some Gypsies, and joined up with them. They were going over the sea, they said. There was a ship waiting for us, and she set sail at once. Come midday we were all very hungry, so

we got out of the ship and lit a fire on the sea, and cooked ourselves a good meal. Then we sailed on, and we reached land just before dark, and there was my caravan waiting on the beach with my old woman in it. Right glad she was to see me, I can tell you, and right glad I was to see her. And I haven't been underground since.

A WICKED FOX

A Story from Syria

A peasant was plowing with two oxen. One of them broke away, and the peasant said, "O wicked ox, if I catch you I will kill you with my knife."

The ox was afraid, and he fled until he came to a place of long, rich grass. The ox stayed there and ate the grass. Abou Hassan, the fox, saw him there and said, "O ox, why do you stay here? This place belongs to a panther. When she finds you here she will strike you dead and eat you."

But the ox only grunted and went on eating the long, rich grass.

So Abou Hassan went to the panther and said, "There is an ox eating your grass."

The panther came to the ox and said, "Why are you here?"

Said the ox, "I am tired of pulling the plow, and I am hungry. I found this place and I wish to eat in it."

The panther said no more and went away. The ox ate the grass for ten days and grew as large as a camel. Then Abou Hassan came to him and said, "The panther has left you in this place to get fat. Soon she will come to eat you. When she comes, look fierce, redden your eyes, and kill her with your horns."

Abou Hassan went to the panther and said, "You have left the ox in your grass, and he has grown fat and fierce. If he sees you he will want to kill you."

The panther growled and went to the grass. The ox looked fierce and reddened his eyes. He thrust with his horns and killed the panther, and she struck with her paw and killed the ox.

Abou Hassan called his wife and children and all his people. They ate the ox and the panther, even the bones, so there was nothing left.

Then Abou Hassan wandered about, looking for more mischief which he could do. He found a sheepskin cloak

A WICKED FOX

in a place where Arabs had camped. He put his head in
the hole of the cloak and spread the cloak over his
shoulders. Then he went into a cave where a panther lived
who was the brother of the panther the ox had killed. The
panther said to him, "Abou Hassan, why have you killed
my sister?"

Abou Hassan answered, "I am not the ox."

The panther said, "It was you who led them to fight."
Then the panther took notice of the sheepskin cloak which
was on Abou Hassan's shoulders. He said, "Will you make
me a cloak like that?"

"O panther, I will," said Abou Hassan, "if you will kill
four sheep and bring them to me."

The panther brought the sheep. Abou Hassan and his
family ate them all and threw the skins into a pit.

The panther came to him and said, "Abou Hassan,
where is the cloak which you were going to make for me?"

"O panther, I need another sheep," he answered.

The panther brought him another sheep, and he made
a good meal of it and threw the skin into a pit.

Presently the panther came and said, "Where is the
cloak, Abou Hassan?"

He ran away, and the panther ran after him. Abou Hassan ran into a small hole. The panther caught his tail and
bit it off. He escaped, but the panther called to him, "I
shall know you again, Abou Hassan. You are the fox that
has no tail."

"Something must be done about this," said Abou Hassan to himself. He looked about until he found a vineyard
full of ripe grapes. Then he went to the other foxes and
said, "If you will tie your tails under your bellies I will
show you where to get ripe grapes."

They did this, so that they seemed to have no tails. Then he led them to the vineyard, where they ate many grapes.

After this Abou Hassan betook himself to the panther. The panther said, "I will kill you, Abou Hassan. You ate the sheep which I gave you but you did not make my cloak."

Abou Hassan answered, "O panther, it was not I. It must have been another fox."

"It was you. I know you because you have no tail."

"But all my people are without tails," answered Abou Hassan.

"Show me then," said the panther.

So Abou Hassan called his people together. The panther could not see their tails, which were tied under their bellies, and he could not tell which fox had eaten the sheep. He did not know what to do.

Then Abou Hassan invited the panther to dinner. He spread a beautiful carpet over a deep pit, and when the panther came he said, "O panther, here is a place of honor for you."

The panther sat on the carpet and fell into the pit, but as he fell he snapped at Abou Hassan and dragged him into the pit. Abou Hassan fell on top of the panther and was not hurt. The panther was killed. Abou Hassan ate him, but he could not get out of the pit, for it was too deep.

Nearby there were women going to market to sell chickens. They had a large basket full of chickens. At nightfall they came to the pit, and they said, "We will lower the basket into this pit, to keep the chickens safe from the foxes, and we will sleep here." This they did.

In the morning they hauled up the basket. Abou Hassan had eaten all the chickens and was asleep in the basket. He sprang out at them, looking very fierce.

The women were frightened and ran away, weeping and wringing their hands because they had lost all their chickens. When Abou Hassan saw this he was very sorry for them. He said, "I have done wrong to steal all their chickens. I will sin no more. I will go to a monastery and become a holy fox."

And this he did.

A DISH OF LABAN

A Story from Syria

A young prince went riding. He rode on and on until he came to a city he had never seen before. He went to the king's palace in that city. The king had a daughter, and when she saw the prince she wished to marry him.

The princess said to him, "Go, ask the king, my father, if you may marry me."

The prince went and asked the king for her. The king said, "How can I know that you are truly a prince, the son of a king?"

The prince said, "Try me in any way you wish."

The king said, "I will." He sent for a dish of laban, which is a dish of sour milk. The king said to the prince, "Here is a dish of laban. Balance it on your head. Climb that palm tree which is outside this palace and throw down two bunches of dates. You must not spill one drop of the laban. Do this and the princess shall be your wife."

The prince told the princess. She pulled a hair from her head and put it into the dish. The laban became solid, and the dish became fixed to the prince's head.

The prince climbed the tree and threw down two bunches of dates. He climbed down again and took the hair from the dish. The laban and the dish became as before. So he went to the king.

The king had watched from a window of the palace. The king said, "Truly this lad is the son of a king or he could not have done this thing without spilling one drop of the laban."

The prince and the princess were married. The king gave them two hundred slaves and loaded ten mules with gold for them.

They went to the prince's city. He found that his father was dead, and he became king in his father's place.

SINKO'S LUCK

A Story from Poland

There was a young man named Sinko who lived with his wife in a little cottage. One day his wife said, "Please grind some corn so that I can make bread."

He took all the wheat there was in the house, and ground it into flour. Then he did a silly thing. He put the bowl of flour outside on the window ledge. He was a very silly young man.

Soon the wind came and blew all the flour away. "You dolt," cried his wife, "you big stupid! You get sillier every day. Now what are we going to do?"

"I will go and find the wind," answered Sinko, "and ask him to give us back our flour."

So off he went. He traveled far and far until he came to a forest. There he saw a man up a tree, blowing the leaves off it.

"Where are you going?" said the man up the tree.

"I'm looking for the thief who stole our flour."

"What is his name?"

"He is the wind," said Sinko.

"I am the wind," said the man up the tree.

"Then please give me back my flour," said Sinko. "It was all we had, and you blew it away after I had put the bowl on our window ledge."

"I'm sorry," said Wind, "I can't give it back to you. It's all scattered. But if you come with me I'll give you something much better."

He blew the last leaf off the tree, and climbed down, and took Sinko to his house.

"I'll give you this magic tablecloth," he said. "If you say to it, 'Tablecloth, unfold yourself—'"

As he spoke the tablecloth spread itself on the table. Plates and knives and forks and glasses came out of the air and arranged themselves, and then filled themselves with wonderful food and drink. It smelled delicious. They had a very good meal. Then Sinko thanked Wind, took the cloth, and set out for home.

When night fell he had still a long way to go, so he stopped at a roadside tavern to find a bed for the night. He drank too much and talked too much. Before going to bed he said to the landlord of the tavern, "You must be sure not to tell my tablecloth to unfold itself."

"Never fear," said the landlord. But he was a bad man who often robbed travelers. As soon as Sinko was asleep he crept into the bedroom and took the tablecloth. Then he told it to unfold itself, and it gave him a splendid meal.

"I cannot part with this," he said to himself. He found another cloth which looked much the same, and put it beside Sinko's bed.

In the morning Sinko set off again, and that afternoon he reached home.

"See what Wind has given me," he said to his wife. "If you tell it to unfold it will do wonders. You try it."

"Oh no," she answered. "You know how to make it work. You do it."

"Well, you'll see. Tablecloth, unfold yourself!"

The tablecloth took no notice. Again and again Sinko shouted at it, but nothing happened.

"The wind has tricked me," he said at last. "I'll go and talk to him." So he set off and walked until he found Wind at the edge of the forest.

"This is strange," said Wind, when he had heard the story. "Someone must have stolen that tablecloth. Come with me, and I will give you something even better."

When they reached Wind's house Wind gave Sinko a lamb. "This is a magic lamb," he said. "If you tell it to shake itself it will pour golden coins out of its mouth until you tell it to stop."

"Thank you, Wind," said Sinko. "Now we shall never have to go hungry again."

He picked up the lamb and set off. As soon as he was out in the fields he put the lamb down on the grass and said, "Lamb, lamb, shake yourself!" At once the lamb poured golden coins out of its mouth, until there was a heap of them. Then Sinko cried, "Stop!" and it stopped. He stuffed his pockets full of gold, picked up the lamb, and went on. "This time the magic certainly works," he said to himself.

As he was passing the tavern the landlord saw him and called out, "Come in and have a drink."

In he went, and the landlord gave him a large glass of brandy. He threw down a gold coin and ordered more. He went on drinking too much and talking too much, for he was a very silly young man. At last he staggered off to bed, saying to the landlord, "You mustn't tell my lamb to shake itself." He had just enough sense left to take the lamb into his bedroom with him.

Very soon he was snoring loudly. Then the landlord crept in and took the lamb to his own room. "Shake yourself!" he said. The lamb poured out gold pieces until the floor was covered with them and the landlord told it to stop.

"I must have this lamb," said the landlord to himself. He went to the nearest farm and bought a lamb of the right size, which he put in Sinko's bedroom.

Next day the silly young man set off, clutching the wrong lamb. When he reached home he emptied all the gold out of his pockets on to the table, and his wife was delighted.

"Oh, but this is nothing," he said. "See what I'm going to do with this lamb!"

He put the lamb on the floor and cried "Lamb, lamb, shake yourself!"

The lamb took no notice, but lay down and went to sleep. Nothing he could say made any difference.

"Wind has tricked me again," he cried. "I'll go and talk to him!"

He was so angry that he didn't stop walking until he had found Wind.

"Why have you come back?" said Wind. "What is wrong now?"

"Do you think I'm a fool?" roared Sinko. "Why do you treat me like this?" And he told his story.

"Ah," said Wind, "I think I understand. When I was blowing around the tavern this morning I heard a lamb bleating. But we can soon put it right."

He cut a heavy stick from a tree and gave it to Sinko.
"If you tell this cudgel to strike," said Wind, "it will go on
beating until you tell it to stop. But you mustn't say a
word to it before you reach the tavern."

Sinko thanked him and went off with the cudgel under
his arm. As he was passing the tavern the landlord called
him in, as before. Once again he drank far too much and
talked far too much, but this time he knew what he was
doing. So when he was going to bed he said to the landlord, "Don't tell my cudgel to strike. Don't say anything to
it."

"Trust me," said the landlord. "You ought to know me
by this time."

As soon as he heard Sinko snoring he crept into the
bedroom and carried off the cudgel to his own room.

"Strike, strike!" he said to it.

Strike it did. It belabored the wicked landlord until he was howling with pain. He couldn't stop it. He ran roaring into Sinko's bedroom, with the cudgel following.

"Stop it," he howled. "Call it off! It's killing me! I'll give you back your tablecloth and your lamb if you'll stop it."

Sinko sat up in bed and called off the cudgel. "Now bring me the tablecloth and the lamb at once, or you shall be beaten to death," he said.

The landlord brought them into the bedroom and fled. Sinko slept in peace that night, for he knew that the landlord would not dare to come near him.

Next morning he set out for home, and when he arrived he said to his wife, "Now all is well. Watch!"

He cried, "Lamb, lamb, shake yourself!" and the lamb poured out gold pieces until he told it to stop.

"Tablecloth, unfold yourself!" he cried. It spread itself over the table and the most wonderful feast you can imagine came out of the air.

"How splendid!" said Sinko's wife, and she kissed him. "You aren't such a silly man after all."

They had a beautiful house built for themselves with some of their gold, and if they haven't gone away they are living there happily still.

EIGHTEEN RABBITS

A Story from Wales and Syria

In a cottage in the hills there lived an old widow and her
three sons. When the oldest was grown up he said,
"Mother, there is nothing for me here. I must go out into
the world to seek my fortune."

"Very well, Evan, my son," she said. She made him a
cake to put into his knapsack, and he said good-bye and
off he went, barefooted and bareheaded as he was.

When he had walked all the morning along the hot,
dusty road he sat down under a tree. He ate his cake,
and had a drink of water from a stream. Then he went on.

At sunset he came to a fine, big house. He pushed
open the gate and went up the drive to the front door and
pulled the bell.

The master of the house answered the door himself.
"What do you want?" he said.

"Please, sir, I want work," said Evan.

"And what can you do?"

"Any job about the house, sir, I think, sir," answered the lad.

"Well, then, go around to the kitchen door and ask the cook to give you supper and a bed," said the master. "In the morning we'll see what you can do."

So Evan did that. The cook gave him a pot of ale, and as much good bread and beef and mustard as he could eat. Then he slept the night in a feather bed.

Now the master of that house had a pretty daughter. She wanted to get married, and her father and mother wanted her to get married, for they had no son of their own. But there were no likely lads for miles around; they had all gone to the wars. So the master wondered if Evan would do and made up his mind to put him to the test.

Next morning, when Evan had had a good breakfast of bacon and eggs, and had washed himself under the kitchen pump, the master said to him, "Now, Evan, you must take my rabbits out into the fields to graze. I have eighteen rabbits, and if you don't bring them all back at sunset I shall turn you out of the house."

He blew a silver whistle and all his rabbits came lolloping to him, eighteen black and white rabbits with white tails bobbing. Evan got a meat pie and an apple from the cook for his dinner and took the rabbits to a field near the house. They wandered all over the field while Evan sat beside a little well and watched them.

Presently he got very hungry, so he took out the meat pie and began to eat it. Then a little old woman came hobbling across the field to him. "Good morning," she said. "Will you give me a morsel to eat? I'm very hungry."

"No," said Evan, "I won't. There isn't enough for me. Go away." So the old woman sadly hobbled off.

After his dinner Evan fell sound asleep, and when he woke the sun was setting, so he looked around for the rabbits. He searched all over the field, and the next field and the next. Three rabbits were all he could find, and he had to take them back to the house, feeling very scared.

"You rascal," roared the master in a fury, "you good-for-nothing scamp. You've lost fifteen of my rabbits. Get out!" Seizing a stick he belabored Evan, who ran away as fast as he could, and never stopped running until the house was out of sight. Then he went on slowly up the road.

A few days after this the widow's second son said that he too must go and seek his fortune. He went along the road until he came to the fine, big house and there everything happened to him just as it had happened to his brother Evan. Then he too went on sadly and slowly up the road.

A week later the youngest son, Ivor, said to his mother, "My two brothers must have made their fortunes by now. I must go after them."

"My poor boy," said his mother, "you are too young. And what shall I do, all alone here? There will be no one to bring firewood from the forest and water from the spring."

"I won't stay away for long, Mother," said Ivor. "Please make me a cake and let me go."

"You can't go until you have brought me this sieve full of water from the spring," she said. She put the sieve into his hands and said to herself, "No one can fill a sieve with water. This will keep him here."

Ivor scratched his head and said, "Well, I will try."

Off he went to the spring. There was a robin pecking

121

about, so he threw some crumbs from his pocket to the robin. Then he filled the sieve with water, and of course it all ran out through the holes. "Oh," he said, "what can I do?"

The robin redbreast had been watching him.

"It's easy," said the robin. "Cover the bottom of the sieve with leaves, then spread clay over the leaves, and then it will hold water."

"Thank you, Robin," said Ivor. He did as the robin had said. Then he carried the sieve full of water to his mother.

So there was nothing else for it. Go he must. But before he went he filled every jug and pot and kettle with water, and brought a great heap of firewood from the forest. Then he put his cake in his knapsack, hugged his mother, and set off along the hot, dusty road.

Presently he came to the fine, big house. The master and mistress and their daughter were all looking out of a window as he came up the drive. "What a good-looking boy," the daughter said to herself, and she smiled at him. "Now this *is* a likely lad," said the master to himself, and he went to the door.

"Good evening," said he. "What do you want?"

"Good evening, sir," answered Ivor. "If you please, I am trying to find work."

"Come in," said the master. "You can go and wash while I find you a good suit of clothes and a pair of shoes. When you've put them on, the cook will give you supper in the kitchen and show you where to sleep. I'll find you work in the morning."

In the morning the master said, "Now, Ivor, I have eighteen rabbits. You must take them into the field be-

side the house so that they can graze there all day. At sunset you must bring them back. If you don't bring them all I shall drive you out of the house. If you do bring them all back you will be the first man to do so. Then you shall marry my daughter, if you are both willing."

The master blew his silver whistle and the eighteen black and white rabbits came lolloping to him, with their white tails bobbing. Ivor took them into the field and then sat down beside the little well to watch them.

When the sun was high in the sky he felt hungry, so he took out the meat pie which the cook had given him. Then a little old woman came in at the gate and hobbled across the field.

"Good morning, ma'am," said Ivor.

"Good morning, young sir," said she. "Could you spare me a morsel of your pie? I am very hungry."

"You look very hungry," said Ivor, "and very tired. If you sit down here you can have half the pie and half the apple, and a good drink of water from the well."

"Thank you kindly," she said.

So they ate their dinner together, and afterward the old woman said, "Now if you would like to walk around and stretch your legs I will look after the rabbits."

So he did that, and when he came back at sunset the old woman took a silver whistle from her pocket and blew it. Most of the rabbits were out of sight, but soon they came lolloping, by ones and twos, until all eighteen of them were gathered at Ivor's feet. Then he thanked the old woman, and took the rabbits back to the house.

The master and mistress and the daughter came out to meet him. "Oh, well done, Ivor," said the master. "You've brought them all." The four of them had a long talk until at last the master said, "Now, if you go to the cook you can get your supper."

Off went Ivor. As soon as he was gone the master said, "I think this young man will suit us."

"So do I," said the mistress.

"And so do I," said the daughter.

After that it wasn't very long before the two were married. They lived happily in the fine, big house and Ivor looked after his mother and the old woman. But the two brothers did not come back, so I suppose they are still seeking their fortunes.

SMALL WHITE STONES

A Story from Wales

There were three sisters living by themselves in a lonely cottage, and they lived there happily enough. One day a little old woman in a red cloak came and knocked at the door. The three sisters answered it.

"I am very thirsty," said the old woman. "Please will you give me a cup of tea?"

"Yes, of course," said the youngest sister. "You are very welcome."

"No," said the other two sisters. "We haven't got enough for ourselves. Go away." And they shut the door in her face.

The old woman called to them through the door. "I will bind your head and your eyes," she said. "I will bind your whole body." And with that she hobbled away.

The three sisters went on living there happily enough, until all their money was gone. Then the oldest sister said, "I must go out and find work. You two must stay here to look after the house. As long as the spring goes on flowing you will know that all is well with me. But if it stops flowing you will know that I'm in trouble. Then one of you must come to help me."

She said good-bye and off she went. She walked on and on until she came into the land where the cock never crows and the Devil never blows his horn. There was a fence across the path, and by it stood a man in a red jerkin. He was the little old woman's brother. He was watching for the girl, and he spoke first because this gave him power over her. "Good day to you," he said. "Are you looking for work?"

"Yes," said she.

He opened a gate in the fence. "Go up this hill," said he, "and you will get work."

She began to climb the hill. All the way up there were small white stones beside the path.

"Stop and look," cried one white stone.

She stopped and looked. She was turned into a small white stone. So did the little old woman bind first her head and eyes with a spell and then bind her whole body.

Meanwhile the two younger sisters had been watching the spring. For three days it went on running. Then when the second sister went out to look at it she found that it had stopped.

"Our sister is in trouble," she said. "I must go to her. You must watch the spring. It will run while I am safe and stop flowing if I am in trouble. Then you must come to me."

She went on her way, and the spring began to run again. She went on and she went on until she came to the land where the cock never crows and the Devil never blows his horn. There she met the man in the red jerkin.

"Good day to you," said he, speaking first. "Are you looking for work?"

"No," said she, "I am looking for my sister."

"Your sister is up yonder," said he, opening the gate in the fence. "She has found work and is doing well."

The second sister thanked him and went up the hill.

"Stop," cried a white stone, but she did not stop.

"Look!" cried another stone. "Here is your sister!"

At that she stopped and looked about her. She was turned into a small white stone.

Next morning the youngest sister found that the spring had stopped running. "My poor sisters!" she cried, and burst into tears.

But very soon she dried her tears and set out on the road which she had seen them follow.

She went on and on until she met with the man in the red jerkin.

"Good day," she said. "Can you tell me where to find my two sisters?"

He was very angry, because she had spoken first; he had no power over her. But he said, "Yes, you'll find them both up this hill." He opened the gate, and she went through.

As she climbed, a small white stone cried out to her, "Stop!" She went on.

"Look!" cried another stone. Still she went on.

"Stop and look!" cried a third stone. "Your sisters are here."

"Then kiss them for me," said she, and went on up the hill.

At the top she found a beautiful cottage, and in the doorway stood the little old woman in the red cloak. She fell on her knees at the girl's feet.

"You have broken the spell," she said. "I have no more power."

At that all the small white stones turned into girls, and they all ran away down the hill and out of the little gate, except for the two sisters. They went up the hill to the cottage. They kissed the youngest sister and thanked her.

"Now," said the old woman to the youngest sister, "everything here is yours. You are the mistress now." She showed her a room in the cottage which was full of gold

coins and precious jewels of every kind. Then she hobbled away and was never seen again.

The two older sisters wanted to go back to their own cottage, so the youngest gave them two large bags stuffed with money and jewels. "If ever you are in trouble," she said, "let me know."

They said good-bye and went happily on their way, but the youngest sister stayed in the beautiful cottage on top of the hill.

GOGGLE-EYES

A Story from Wales

In a hut among the mountains there lived a widow and her two sons. One winter day when it was snowing hard the old woman wanted a few sticks to make a better fire and bake some cakes, but there was only one stick left.

"Will you go into the wood and get some sticks?" she said to her sons.

They didn't want to leave the fireside and go out into the snow, but she begged them and begged them. At last the elder son got up and looked out of the door, but when he saw how deep the snow was he shut the door and sat down again.

But now the last stick had been put on the fire; it was going out and the hut was getting cold. So presently the elder son, grumbling loudly, got up and went out. He

plowed through the soft, deep snow into the wood to gather any sticks he could find; but the first thing he saw was a tall watchtower. He was very surprised, for he'd never seen a tower there before. He walked all around it, looking for a door, and found there wasn't one. Then he walked around it again, looking it over carefully, and this time he saw a little window, high up near the roof. At that moment the window flew open, and a large head with great goggle-eyes looked down at him.

"Hi, young man," said the head. "Will you do me a kindness? There's a jug beside the spring in the wood. Will you fill it with water and bring it to me? I can't get out."

"What will you give me, Goggle-Eyes?" said the lad.

"I've nothing to give," said the head. "I'm very poor."

"Then get your water yourself, Goggle-Eyes," said the lad, and went on to look for sticks. But all the sticks in the wood leaped up out of the snow and rushed at him, and beat him until he ran home, yelling all the way. He tumbled in at the door of the hut.

"What's the matter, my boy?" cried his mother. "What's happened?"

"Gamekeepers!" he said, rubbing his bruises. "There were gamekeepers in the wood, and they wouldn't let me get any sticks. They beat me and drove me away."

"Oh, dear," said the old woman. "The fire's nearly out, I can't bake my cakes, and soon we shall all freeze. What are we to do?"

The younger brother, whose name was David, got up from his stool beside the hearth. "I must go and see if I have any better luck," he said.

He went into the wood and soon came to the tall tower, which surprised him very much.

"Where did this come from?" he said to himself. He walked around the tower, the little window flew open, and Goggle-Eyes looked down at him.

"Hi, young man," said Goggle-Eyes. "Please will you fetch an old gentleman a little water in the jug that's beside the spring?"

"That I will," said David, and came back very soon with the jug full of water.

Goggle-Eyes lowered a rope from the window, and David tied the jug to it. Then Goggle-Eyes hauled up the jug, thanked David, and shut the window.

David gathered a heap of sticks, and soon had as many as he could carry. Then he looked round. The tower had vanished!

A voice behind him said, "David!"

He turned, and there stood a tiny dwarf, magnificently dressed.

"I am the king of the forest," said the dwarf, "but a wicked enchanter shut me up in that tower. You have broken the spell and set me free."

He took a ring from his finger and gave it to David. "When you want anything," said the king, "rub this ring and you shall have your wish."

"Thank you kindly, sir, Your Majesty," said David, and put the ring into his pocket. The king vanished, and David turned to his sticks. Before he could touch them they gathered themselves into a neat bundle and tied themselves up, so it was easy for him to carry them home.

His mother was delighted when she saw how many he had brought. "These will make a fine blaze," she said. And very soon the hut was warm again and the cakes were beautifully baked.

Now there was a grand castle not far away from the widow's hut, and the lord of that castle was in great distress. A wicked witch had taken all his money and crammed it into a huge sack. She had put the sack at the back of a cave near the castle, and she had lit a magic fire which filled the mouth of the cave and blazed so fiercely, day and night, that no one could get into the cave.

So the lord of the castle proclaimed that he would give his youngest daughter in marriage to any man who could bring the sack of money out of the cave. Young men came from all over the country to try their fortune, but it was no use. Some of them gave up when they saw that terrible fire. Some tried to get through it and were badly burned. David's elder brother tried, and he couldn't face the flames.

"Well," said David, "now it's my turn."

"Don't be silly," said his mother. "No one can get through that magic fire. You'll get all your clothes scorched off your back."

But David thought of his magic ring. He went down to the cave. He rubbed the ring and wished that the fire should not burn him. Then he walked through the flames, and they did not even singe his clothes. The sack was almost too heavy for him to lift, but he got it onto his back somehow and staggered back through the fire, still unhurt. He carried the sack up to the castle, dumped it outside the great door, and ran away as fast as he could.

Now the lord and his three daughters had been looking out of a window and had seen what David did.

"Who is that young beggarman who has rescued our gold?" said the lord.

None of his daughters knew. But the youngest daughter said to herself, "He may be poor, but he's very brave, and very good-looking too."

Meanwhile David had gone home. Now that he knew how well his ring worked he wished the drafty old wooden hut to be turned into a beautiful, cozy cottage. He wished fine new clothes onto his mother, his brother, and himself. He wished that they should always have enough to eat.

In a flash all these wishes were granted, and David's mother and brother were so amazed that they could only stare at everything without saying a word. He didn't show them his ring or tell them that it was he who had worked the magic. But they soon settled down to enjoy all their new things and all their good food.

Meanwhile the lord had sent his servants far and wide to search for David, and it wasn't long before they came to the cottage and found him. Then the lord sent his best carriage, drawn by four splendid black horses, to fetch David, and he was driven to the castle in fine style.

"Welcome, David," said the lord, and told the butler to bring him a tankard of ale.

"Welcome, David," said the three daughters, and David thought the youngest must be the most beautiful girl in the world. She smiled at him, and he rubbed the ring in his pocket, saying to himself, "I wish this lovely girl would fall in love with me."

So she did, of course, and they got married. David wished a splendid house for them, and they were very happy. And David saw to it that his mother and brother never wanted for anything.

SQUIRREL AND FOX

A Story from Wales

There were two brothers living in a village down in England who could not get any work to do.

"Let us go and look for work," said Will, who was the older.

"But shall we have good fortune if we do?" said Jack. "Let us go and ask the little old woman who lives in the cave. She will tell us."

So off they went. There was a great stone in the mouth of the cave, but they called to the old woman.

"Aha," she answered, "I was expecting you. Please roll away the stone."

They did this and then she said, "I cannot walk now. Do you come in and carry me outside."

They carried her out and set her down in the sunshine.

"I know what you want to ask me, and I know the answer. Jack, I will give you this stone, and it will bring good fortune to you both." She put something into his hand. He found it was a stone no bigger than a halfpenny. "Put it in your pocket and do not take it out until you come to three roads. Then it will tell you what to do."

They thanked her and carried her back into her cave. Then they got ready and set out along the road. Presently it divided into three. They stopped. Jack took out the stone; one side was black as coal and the other was as yellow as gold. A voice whispered in his ear, "Toss the stone. If it falls with the golden side up, take the right-hand road. If the black side is up take the road to the left."

Jack tossed the stone high in the air and it fell at his feet with the golden side uppermost.

"You must take the road to the left," he said to his brother. "I'll go to the right, and let us meet here in a month and a day."

"Agreed," said Will, so they said good-bye and parted.

Jack walked on and on, and presently he heard a girl's voice calling for help. He ran to the top of the hill, and there below was a hideous giant, under a tree. He had hung a rope over one of the boughs, with a noose in the end of it, and he was trying to put the noose around the neck of a beautiful girl.

"Save me, save me!" she cried to Jack.

What did Jack do? He took the little stone from his pocket and threw it at the giant. It struck him on the fore-head and he fell dead.

The girl thanked Jack and kissed him and said, "This wicked giant was going to hang me because I would not marry his ugly son, whom I hate."

Jack took the stone from the giant's forehead. A voice whispered in his ear, "Leave the giant where he is. Put the stone beside his left foot. Then he will never be seen again."

Jack did this, and the giant's dead body disappeared.

What did the girl say then? She said, "Come with me to the giant's castle and I will give you a bag of gold for saving my life."

She took Jack to the castle. The great door was wide open but there was no one in the place. "His son is out hunting," said the girl. She gave Jack the bag of gold pieces. "You saved my life," she said. "You shall make your fortune. A fox and a squirrel will tell you how to do it."

So they said good-bye and Jack went on, day after day, over the mountains until he came to the sea. He was very hungry and thirsty now, and the bag of gold seemed to get heavier and heavier. But there was no house in sight, nowhere he could buy food. Suddenly he saw a man coming toward him, and it was his brother Will.

"Greeting!" said Will. "What's in your bag?"

"Gold pieces," answered Jack. "What is in yours?"

"Food," answered Will. "Good beef and good bread and two bottles of good red wine. I'm hungry. I'm going to eat."

"Will you give me some?" asked Jack. "I am dying of hunger and thirst."

"Yes," answered Will. "You shall have half of all I've got if you'll give me your bag of gold."

Well, they argued about it, but poor Jack was so thirsty that he gave in. When they had eaten up all Will's food they parted again, but now Will had the gold and Jack had nothing except a good meal inside him.

He went on till he came to a wood and there he sat down to rest in the shade of a big tree. Presently he heard voices on the other side of the tree.

"Good day to you, Squirrel," said one voice. "Good day to you, Fox," said the other. "What is the news of the wide world?"

"Oh," said Fox. "You know there's a city on the other side of this mountain. All the people there are going to die of thirst because their fountain has dried up. But if they only knew, all they have to do is to dig a well in front of the clock tower. They'd find all the water they want."

"And do you know, old chicken-stealer," said Squirrel, "that the mayor of that city lost his sight last week?"

"No, I hadn't heard that," answered Fox. "But how silly humans are! They've only got to rub the mayor's eyes with leaves from this tree and he will get his eyesight back, as good as ever."

"Now I'll tell you something else," said Squirrel. "The princess in that city has horns growing out of the sides of her head, and none of the doctors can help her. The queen has offered a rich reward to anyone who can get rid of them."

"That is easy," said Fox, "if they only knew. If the princess eats three apples from the tree which grows beside the fountain the horns will disappear. Is that all your news?"

"That's all," said Squirrel. "Good-bye, old rabbit-hunter." And he scampered up the tree.

"Good-bye, nutcracker," said Fox, and he ran into the wood.

"This is the good fortune which the beautiful girl promised me," said Jack to himself. "I must go to that city." He pulled a dozen leaves from the tree and set off.

When he had found the mayor's house he knocked boldly at the front door. A servant answered, and Jack said, "I can cure the mayor's blindness. Please take me to him."

"Oh, can you?" said the servant. "Nobody else can. But I suppose you might as well try. This way."

He led Jack to a room where the poor blind mayor was sitting. "Your Worship," said Jack, "I can give you back your sight. All I need is a bowl of hot water and a large clean feather."

They were soon brought. Jack soaked the leaves in the water, dipped the feather in it, and drew the feather across the mayor's eyes. In a few seconds he could see as well as ever.

"This is marvelous!" he cried. "Thank you, thank you. And now, what is your fee?"

"If Your Worship would give me a bag of gold—"

"With all the pleasure in the world," cried the mayor, and very soon a heavy bag was in Jack's hands.

"There's another thing, Your Worship," said Jack. "Folk tell me your city has no water."

"Yes, it's nearly all gone," said the mayor. "We shall soon be dying of thirst."

"If Your Worship will come with me I will show you where to find water," said Jack.

He led the way to the clock tower, and stood in front of it. "Tell your men to dig here," he said.

The mayor sent for workmen, who stripped to the waist and dug with a will. They did not have to dig very deep. Soon they found a spring of fresh, clean water.

Everyone was delighted. All the church bells in the city rang for joy and the mayor thanked Jack again and again, and gave him three bags of gold pieces.

"I'm doing well in this city," he said to himself. "And there is still the princess."

He bought a big haversack to carry all his gold pieces,

he bought some clothes from a doctor and put them on, and he gathered three fine apples from the tree beside the fountain which had dried up. Then he went to the palace.

When he said he was a doctor he was taken at once to see the princess. "Can you cure me?" she cried. "Can you take these dreadful horns from my head? All our doctors have failed."

Jack bowed low. "Yes, Your Highness," said he. "I can do it. It will take three days." He took an apple from his haversack. "This is a magic apple," he said. "You must eat it today, and tomorrow morning I will call again."

Bowing once more he came away, leaving the princess munching the apple.

When she got up next morning the first thing she did was to look in her mirror. The horns had become smaller. She clapped her hands for joy and ran to show the king and queen.

Jack came again. The princess was so grateful that she sprang up and gave him her hand. He gave her another apple.

Next morning he came for the third time. The horns were smaller still. The princess was almost crying for joy. "Here is the last of the apples, Your Highness. Tomorrow I will come for the last time, and by then the horns will be gone altogether."

Next morning when the princess woke up she jumped out of bed and ran to her mirror. The horns were gone! She ran to show the king and queen and soon the whole palace was buzzing with the good news. "The princess's horns have gone!"

When Jack came he was greeted with cheers. The king and queen and princess shook him warmly by the hand.

"What is your fee, master doctor?" asked the king.

"Five bags of gold pieces, if it please Your Majesty," answered Jack.

The five bags were soon brought, and Jack went away with as much gold as he could carry.

When he reached the crossroads it was midnight, so he lay down under a bush and slept till morning.

When he woke up he heard footsteps on the road, and there was his brother coming.

"Good day to you, Will," said he. "How have you got on?"

"Very badly," answered Will. "I've spent all the gold you gave me and I haven't a penny left."

"Well, I have enough for us both," said Jack.

So they went on together, very friendly. When they reached the little old woman's cave they gave her a handful of gold pieces, which made her very happy. Then they bought themselves a nice house and lived there together, with a little maidservant to look after them.

BALDPATE

A Story from Turkey

Once upon a time, long ago, there was a ship sailing on the
Black Sea, and she put into a little port to get fresh
water. The captain went ashore. He saw half a dozen
lads on the quay, and one was taller and stronger than
all the others, but he had no hair on his head.

"Baldpate," called the captain, and the lad with no hair
came to him.

"Could you tell me where to get water for my ship?"
asked the captain.

"I will show you, sir," said Baldpate, and he took the
captain and his men to the village fountain. The men
filled their cask with water and carried it away.

The captain liked the look of Baldpate. "Will you join
my ship?" he said.

"You must ask my mother, sir," answered Baldpate, and he led the way to the wooden hut in which he lived with his widowed mother.

"Good day," said the captain to her. "Will you let your son join my ship? I would give you his first month's pay now."

"Do you want to go?" she said to Baldpate.

"That I do, Mother."

"Then you can have him, sir," she said.

So Baldpate became a sailor.

Far away across the Black Sea lived the king of that country, in a grand palace near the seashore. One day the king's son was out walking when he met a dervish, a holy man, who was trying to sell a portrait of a very beautiful girl. The prince bought it, and the dervish hurried away.

The prince set down the portrait and looked at it and looked at it until he fell wildly in love with the girl. At last he said to himself, "I must marry that girl or die."

He took the portrait to the palace. No one could tell him who the girl was. Calling two of his servants to follow him he went to the fountain in the village near the palace. There he set up the portrait and left the servants to guard it. "Sooner or later," he said to them, "someone will come for water who recognizes the portrait. Bring him to me."

All day the servants kept watch, and toward evening Baldpate came with a party of men to get water for the ship.

"Oh," cried Baldpate, "that portrait is very like her. But she is even more beautiful."

"Do you know this lady?" said one of the servants.

"That I do," answered Baldpate, "we grew up together."

"Then you must come with us to see the prince." And in spite of his protests they marched him off to the palace, with the portrait.

"Do you know this lady?" said the prince.

"Yes, my lord," answered Baldpate. "Her name is Denya. We played together when we were little."

"Where is she to be found?" asked the prince. "I want to marry her."

"She lives in a lonely house by the shore, far away across the sea. As for marrying, my lord, her father keeps her there because he will not let her marry anyone."

"I must marry her or die of love," said the prince. "Tell me how to find her."

Baldpate thought for a while. At last he said, "It could be done, my lord, if you would fit out your finest galleon, gild her from stem to stern, give her brightly colored sails, and choose your best seamen to man her, with twenty good musicians, for Denya loves music. There must be a princely cabin for you. Most important of all, everything must be done as I wish it done, or we shall fail."

The prince agreed to all this and very soon the galleon set sail, with Baldpate in command.

For seven days and seven nights they sailed across the sea. Then they came at daybreak to the girl's house, which was very near the seashore.

"I will walk the deck," said Baldpate. "All the rest of you must stay below, out of sight. But when I have got her to come aboard and taken her down to the prince's cabin, you must set sail so quietly that she does not hear you. So we will carry her off and then I will take the prince to her."

The sun was shining brightly. Very soon the girl came out of her house and walked along the seashore. She was very surprised to see a strange ship which shone with gold from stem to stern. There was only one man on deck, so she went as close as she could to look.

Then Baldpate called to her, "Denya, don't you remember me?"

"Baldpate!" she cried. "Indeed I do."

"Won't you come aboard, to talk to me and to see my wonderful ship?"

She laughed. "I'll come if you'll fetch me."

He fetched her in a little boat. He showed her around the deck, and then took her down to the prince's cabin, which was empty. They sat and talked, until the prince could stay away no longer. He came into the cabin.

Denya sprang to her feet in alarm. "Who is this?" she cried.

"This is the prince of Baikan," answered Baldpate, "my royal master. He will not harm you."

The prince bowed low and kissed her hand. She thought him very charming.

"Here are wine and sweetmeats," said Baldpate, "and I will ask the prince's musicians to play to you. Let us enjoy ourselves."

He told the musicians to play their sweetest music outside the cabin door. Denya was enchanted by it all. She did not hear the sails being hoisted or feel the ship moving gently forward. But presently she rose. "I must go," she said. "I expect my father to come home early this morning. He must not know I have been out."

She went on deck, followed by the prince and Baldpate. They were already far from the shore and her house was only a speck. She burst into tears.

"Oh, Baldpate, Baldpate," she sobbed. "What have you done to me? Oh, what shall I do? Shall I throw myself into the sea?"

But did she? No, she went and sat down beside the prince.

"Do not be afraid," said the prince. "We shall not harm you. I have loved you since I first saw your portrait. Will you marry me?"

"I—I will tell you later," she said.

But before night came she had said yes and everyone on the ship was very happy. There was music and dancing on the deck.

Next morning early Baldpate was alone on the forecastle when three birds perched in the rigging above his head.

"O bird, O bird," croaked the first.

"What is it, O bird?" croaked the second.

"The prince and Denya are happy, O bird, but when they reach land a small boat will come to take them ashore, the boat will capsize and they will both be drowned. If anyone speaks of this he will be turned into stone up to his knees."

"O bird, O bird," croaked the third.

"What is it, O bird?"

"If the prince and Denya escape drowning, the palace gateway will fall on them and crush them to death. And if anyone speaks of this he will be turned into stone up to the heart."

"O bird, O bird," croaked the second.

"What is it, O bird?"

"If they escape this, a dragon will come that night and kill the prince. And if anyone speaks of this he will be turned into stone from head to foot."

Then the birds flew away, still croaking, and Baldpate was left wondering what to do. No one else had heard the birds talking.

When they reached the land of Baikan the king and queen, the prince's parents, sent a boat to meet the ship, but Baldpate gave the ship's helmsman orders to steer straight for the shore. He ran the ship up onto the beach and helped the prince and Denya to climb down the side.

They went in procession to the palace, with flags waving and music playing, and the king and queen came out to greet them. Before they reached the gateway Baldpate stopped them. "The gate must be pulled down," he ordered.

"But why?" cried the king, angrily.

"That I cannot tell you, sire," answered Baldpate, "but

the prince promised that I should be obeyed in everything."

So the gateway was pulled down.

That evening the palace buzzed with preparations for the grand wedding which was to take place next day. Only Baldpate was unhappy. When night came he said to the prince, "I must sleep in your room tonight, my lord."

The prince did not like it, but he had to give way, because he had promised that all Baldpate's orders should be obeyed. A bed was made up for Baldpate and he lay there wide awake while the prince slept soundly.

At midnight there was a rush of wings, and a hideous green dragon with seven heads flew in at the open window. Baldpate sprang to his feet, drew his sword, and stood guard over the sleeping prince. The dragon roared with fury, turned, and flew out again.

The prince woke and found Baldpate leaning over him, sword in hand. He leaped out of bed. "Help, help!" He called.

Servants came running in. "Arrest him!" cried the prince. "Arrest Baldpate! He was going to kill me. *That's* why he wanted to sleep in my room."

Next morning Baldpate, well guarded, was brought before the king, who was very angry.

"What have you to say for yourself?" demanded the king.

"Nothing, sire," answered Baldpate. He knew that if he explained he would be turned into stone.

"Nothing!" roared the king. "He meant to kill my son, and he has nothing to say! Take him away and cut off his head!"

The guards seized him and led him away. He said to himself, "It would be better to be turned into stone." He said to the guards, "Take me back to the king. There is something I must say to him."

They took him back. Baldpate told the king about the three birds he had heard talking. When he had explained why he beached the ship he was turned into stone up to his knees. When he went on to tell about the gate he was turned into stone up to his heart. Then he told how the dragon came to kill the prince, and he was turned into stone altogether.

The king and the prince were full of sorrow now, and Denya wept. They had a splendid tomb built for the statue, but there was nothing more they could do.

After the wedding the prince grew more and more restless. At last he said to his bride. "Baldpate gave his life to save ours. I must search the world until I find how to bring him back to life. I shall have no peace until I do."

So the prince set out. He went walking, walking, far and wide. At long last he came back to the fountain in Baldpate's village. There he lay down and slept, and Baldpate came to him in a dream.

"Take a handful of earth from beside this fountain and scatter it on my tomb," said Baldpate.

The prince took the earth, and went back to the palace and sprinkled it on the tomb. Baldpate opened his eyes and stretched himself. "I have been sleeping very soundly," he said, and he stepped out of the tomb.

What rejoicing there was then! The king and queen, the prince and Princess Denya, could not do enough for Baldpate. They made him a great lord and he lived happily with them in the palace for the rest of his life.

THE GYPSY FIDDLE

A Story from Hungary

He was a very sad Gypsy. He was all alone, he had no food, no money, nowhere to go. Nothing except his fiddle, which was very dear to him, for he made sweet music and loved it.

He was going along a road through the forest, beside a babbling stream, and presently he came to an inn. He stood at the door, and played his sweetest tune and sang his merriest song. Perhaps someone would ask him inside, and give him money or bread and beer. No one came. No one took any notice. He went on his way again, sadder than before.

A gentle breeze had carried his music far, wandering among the bulrushes in the roadside stream, echoing from the forest trees, and the music came to the ears of the

Devil, who was living at that time in an old willow tree beside the stream. When he heard that sweet sound he said to himself, "I must get that fiddle. If I played music like that everybody would follow me."

So he put on a frock coat and a woolen cap to make himself look respectable and stepped out into the road to meet the Gypsy.

"Greeting, O wanderer," said the Devil.

"Greeting," said the Gypsy, "whoever you may be." But he smiled to himself. He knew it was the Devil because the woolen cap did not quite hide his horns.

"No matter who I am," said the Devil. "I can help you. And I will. But you must give me the thing which is most dear to you."

"That is my fiddle," said the Gypsy. "It is all I have."

"Then you must give me your fiddle."

"But what should I do without it?" said the Gypsy.

"I will give you heaps of gold," said the Devil.

The Gypsy thought it over. He loved his fiddle but he was very hungry. At last he said, "I will."

The Devil pulled two tall bulrushes from the stream and gave one to the Gypsy. "That is your horse," he said. "Mount it and follow me."

They mounted their bulrushes and sailed away through the air like birds. They came down in a valley between the mountains. The Devil took the Gypsy's hand and led him to a waterfall. He took up a handful of stones from the pool of water at the foot of the fall. The stones shone like gold. The Gypsy couldn't believe it. He picked up a handful of stones and sand himself. No doubt about it. They were pure gold.

"You have kept your word," he said. "I must keep mine. But let me play a farewell tune on my fiddle first."

He played such a heartrending tune that the Devil could not help himself; he bowed his head and wept.

When it was finished the Gypsy put his lips to one of the openings in the fiddle and drew in a deep breath. He kissed the fiddle and gave it and the bow to the Devil, who took them and vanished in a cloud of smoke.

The Gypsy took a handful of gold and went to the town to buy food and some better clothes, for he was in rags. Then he went back to the waterfall and filled all his pockets with gold. Now he was rich and he ought to have been happy, but he was sad. He missed his fiddle so badly. For three days he sat watching the water and thinking.

Suddenly the Devil appeared. He was very angry. "I've made a bad bargain," he growled. "You have the gold, but the fiddle's useless. When I play it people do not follow me, they run away. It's useless." He threw the fiddle and the bow at the Gypsy, who picked them up with a joyful heart.

"But why is it," said the Devil, "that I can't make music like yours?"

"It is natural," answered the Gypsy. "I promised to sell you the fiddle, but not to sell you my soul. I had breathed my soul into it. I took my soul back before I gave you the fiddle. Listen."

He put his lips to an opening and breathed into it. He tucked the fiddle under his chin and played a tune so merry that even the Devil had to dance madly till it was over. Then, with a scream of fury, he vanished.

So the Gypsy, with his fiddle under his arm and his pockets full of gold, went happily on his way.

That is how a Gypsy outwitted the Devil. And ever since then it is Gypsy fiddlers who have played the wildest, sweetest music.

AUTHOR'S NOTE

The stories in this book are based on folk tales which have been printed in the following: *Gypsy Folk-tales*, edited by Francis Hindes Groome (London, 1899); *The Journal of the Gypsy Lore Society*; and *XXI Welsh Gypsy Folk-tales* by John Sampson, edited by Dora E. Yates (Montgomeryshire, 1933).

I am greatly indebted to the Hon. Secretary of the Gypsy Lore Society, Miss Dora E. Yates, Litt. D., for permission to make use of transcripts in the Society's *Journal* and in John Sampson's collection; and to Mr. Bernard Gilliat-Smith for permission to use the story "Batim the Horse" which he took down in Romani from a Muslim Gypsy in Sofia.

I am much indebted also to Mrs. Margaret Weston, Mrs. Diane Crook, and Mrs. Glenys Carr for valuable help and advice, and to Mrs. Pamela Royds for much illuminating and sympathetic criticism.

The stories have been written down in many countries by students of Gypsy lore and most of them have been translated from tales told in Romani by illiterate Gypsies. The tales vary much from country to country both in style and content, and I have tried to reflect these variations. A few of my stories follow the transcripts almost word for word; most of them, however, have been considerably abridged and adapted to bring them within the scope of the young readers for whom this book is intended. But I have done my best to keep the spirit and flavor of the originals.

Many books have been written about Gypsy life and lore. One of the most fascinating is by Jan Yoors, who wrote the introduction to this book. It is *The Gypsies*, published by Simon and Schuster, 1967, and is an account of his own life among the Gypsies. Professor Walter Starkie, C.M.G., Litt. D., President of the international Gypsy Lore Society, is another writer who has lived with the Gypsies. He is the author of *Raggle-taggle* (London, 1933), *Spanish Raggle-taggle* (London, 1934, 1961), and *In Sara's Tents* (London, 1954).

John W. Hornby's *Gypsies* (New York, 1967) is intended for young readers and gives a comprehensive picture of Gypsy life. Other books of interest are *The Wind on the Heath*, a Gypsy anthology compiled by John Sampson (London, 1930); *Gypsies of Britain*, an introduction to their history, by Brian Vesey-Fitzgerald (London, 1944); *My Gypsy Days: Recollections of a Romani Rawnie*, by Dora E. Yates (London, 1953); and *The Gypsies* by Jean-Paul Clébert, translated from the French by Charles Duff (London, 1963). For specialists *The Journal of the Gypsy Lore Society*, which is published in Edinburgh, is invaluable.

The standard collections of folk tales in English are Francis Hindes Groome's and John Sampson's, noted above, and *A Book of Gypsy Folk-tales* selected by Dora E. Yates (London, 1948). The tales in this last, and in Groome's collection, are drawn from many European countries.

J. H.

1969